The Best Of
Alex
2009

Charles Peattie & Russell Taylor

Masterley Publishing

The Best Of
Alex
2009

First Published in 2009 by MASTERLEY PUBLISHING

Layout and Artwork: Suzette Field

ISBN: 978-1-8537574-5-7

Printed in the UK by CPI William Clowes Beccles NR34 7TL

Our usual gratitude goes to our generous sponsors:

FTSE Group - provider of global equity, fixed income, alternative asset class, responsible investment & investment strategy indices; and Mondo Visione - the leading source of insight and knowledge about the world's exchanges and trading venues.

FOREWORD

The City has come full circle. Back in 1987, when we started writing Alex, Yuppie bankers were making headlines for their greed, insensitivity, arrogance and recklessness. And now - we are somewhat depressed to say, having spent two decades engaged in what we can now see was totally futile satire on these people - they have been back on the front pages again, for all the same reasons.

At the time of writing the City seems unsure as to whether the economic crisis engendered by sub-prime loans and the credit crunch has suddenly somehow just gone away. Have the bankers by some implausible miracle escaped certain annihilation? Or is the financial crisis, like an 80s Hollywood movie villain, only playing dead and poised to leap for their throats again at any moment?

Many satirists, observers, commentators and essentially anyone who didn't earn large bonuses from making highly leveraged punts on the stock market going up, had been thinking that the credit crunch was quite a good thing. Obviously as participants in the global capitalist system we didn't actually want to be propelled back to feudal times, but some sort of a correction seemed overdue. And when all those CDOs, SPVs and other complex financial instruments that the City had been paying themselves huge bonuses for swapping back and forth proved to be worthless we couldn't help thinking of the fable of the Emperor's New Clothes.

What we didn't foresee was that the Emperor, having been publicly mocked for his stupidity and vanity, would come to the conclusion that he actually didn't mind being naked, just so long as he could keep on being Emperor. Alex and his fellow bankers seem to be preparing to go back to business as usual. Well, who can blame them? Nothing particularly bad has happened to them. The taxpayer stumped up to save their jobs, the regulators decided that imposing any form of implementable legislation would render London uncompetitive as a global financial centre and our politicians adjudged that the sense of shame at having been bailed out would be sufficient to prevent the City from ever being so irresponsible again (despite that the fact that the word "shameless" was invented to describe investment bankers). And they even got to keep getting those bonuses.

So whereas at one point it seemed like there might be no need (and indeed no market) for the *Best of Alex 2010*, it now looks like it's back to business as usual for us financial satirists too. And hopefully we'll make a more successful job of it over the next twenty years..

Charles Peattie and Russell Taylor

Alex - Investment banker

Penny - Alex's wife

Christopher - Alex's son

Clive - Alex's colleague

Cyrus - Alex's boss

Bridget - Clive's wife

Rupert - Senior banker

Christian - Euro-banker

Vince - Moneybroker

Alex PEATTIE + TAYLOR

THIS BEAR MARKET IS LOOKING VERY SERIOUS, ALEX... IT'S NOW THREATENING TO AFFECT OUR PERSONAL AS WELL AS BUSINESS LIVES...

I MEAN, I'VE GOT A WIFE AND FOUR YOUNG CHILDREN. THEY'RE REALLY LOOKING FORWARD TO SPENDING OUR CUSTOMARY 2 WEEKS IN THE SOUTH OF FRANCE THIS SUMMER...

BUT I'M AFRAID THIS BUSINESS DOWNTURN IS GOING TO HAVE AN INEVITABLE EFFECT ON THE VIABILITY OF A FAMILY HOLIDAY LIKE THAT...

OH DEAR...

YOU MEAN _YOU_ MIGHT ACTUALLY HAVE TO GO _WITH_ THEM FOR ONCE?

WELL, AS EVERY SINGLE ONE OF MY DEALS HAS BEEN PULLED I CAN'T THINK OF ANY VALID EXCUSE NOT TO...

Alex PEATTIE + TAYLOR

YOU'RE LATE, ALEX. WHAT HAPPENED?

MY TRAIN BROKE DOWN...

WE WERE STUCK FOR ALMOST AN HOUR... I DON'T NEED TO TELL YOU THE EFFECT A HOLD-UP LIKE THAT HAS HAD ON THE EFFICIENCY OF MY WORKING DAY...

I'M SURE YOU CAN EASILY IMAGINE THE BOREDOM, THE EXASPERATION, SITTING THERE USELESSLY, COOPED-UP, UNABLE TO ESCAPE OR ACHIEVE ANYTHING PURPOSEFUL...

I KNOW WHAT YOU MEAN, ALEX...

MEETINGS. QUITE. THAT'S WHERE I'VE GOT TO GO NOW...THANK GOODNESS FOR THAT EXTRA HOUR OF CALM ALONE WITH MY LAPTOP WHERE I GOT MY REAL WORK DONE...

STULTIFYING TEDIUM

Alex PEATTIE + TAYLOR

EATING IN A CITY RESTAURANT WITH ALEX MASTERLEY IS A SPECIAL EXPERIENCE...

IT CERTAINLY IS...

WELL, THANKS TO MY UNSTINTING PATRONAGE OF SUCH ESTABLISHMENTS OVER THE YEARS I'M PERSONALLY KNOWN BY EVERY MAITRE D' IN THE SQUARE MILE...

AND IT SHOWS...

ONE ONLY HAS TO OBSERVE THE LEVEL OF SERVICE AND PERSONAL ATTENTION ACCORDED TO US BY THE STAFF...

YES

WE ARRIVED HALF AN HOUR AGO AND NO ONE'S EVEN TAKEN OUR FOOD ORDER...

WELL, THEY KNOW THERE'S NO HURRY, AS ALEX WILL BE HERE ALL AFTERNOON...

AHEM... TECHNICALLY I'LL BE IN "A SERIES OF CLIENT MEETINGS", CLIVE...

Alex PEATTIE + TAYLOR

CLIVE, I'M SORRY TO TELL YOU: YOU'RE BEING MADE REDUNDANT...

WHAT?!

I GUESS THIS MUST HAVE COME OUT OF LEFT FIELD, BUT, Y'KNOW, SOMETIMES LIFE THROWS YOU A CURVE-BALL...

I'M BEING FIRED AND YOU'RE TALKING BASEBALL...?

HEY, CLIVE...THIS IS TOUGH FOR ME TOO...I'VE GOT TO DELIVER THE NEWS TO A GUY THAT HE HAS TEN MINUTES TO CLEAR HIS DESK AND VACATE IT...

I MEAN, HOW DO YOU BREAK SOMETHING LIKE THAT.?

EASY.

I KNEW THIS STUPID BAT OF HIS WOULD COME IN HANDY ONE DAY.

SECURITY...!

TRASH TRASH

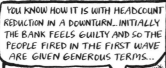

12

ALEX WENT ON HOLIDAY IN SUFFOLK.

Alex PEATTIE + TAYLOR

SO CLIVE GOT SACKED? DID HE SEE IT COMING?

WELL HE'S ALWAYS BEEN VERY PARANOID...

HE'D TAKEN THE CLASSIC PRECAUTION OF SWIPING HIS CORPORATE CREDIT CARD AT THE LOCAL WINE BAR WHERE HE'S FRIENDLY WITH THE MANAGER...

HE PUT IT THROUGH AS A BOGUS CLIENT EXPENSE AT THE TIME AND HE NOW HAS £500 OF CREDIT TO SEE HIM THROUGH HIS REDUNDANCY, WHICH IS HANDY...

CONSIDERING HE SPENDS ALL HIS DAY IN THERE...

WOULDN'T IT BE EASIER TO CONFESS TO HIS WIFE THAT HE'S BEEN SACKED AND STAY AT HOME INSTEAD?

Alex PEATTIE + TAYLOR

OH, HELLO, CLIVE. YOU GOT MADE REDUNDANT YESTERDAY... YES, I'D HEARD... I'M SORRY ABOUT THAT... NO, I DON'T MIND YOU CALLING ME...

WELL, IT'S JUST YOU WERE MY DIRECT COMPETITOR OVER AT CONTINENT BANK... ANYWAY I WAS WONDERING IF THERE WERE ANY JOBS GOING AT YOUR PLACE... OH... YOU HAVE A HIRING FREEZE... NOT TO WORRY... THANKS...

WELL, THAT WAS HUMILIATING... BUT: THINK POSITIVE, CLIVE... THE NEXT STAGE IS TO PHONE MY TOP CLIENTS AND REASSURE THEM THAT I'LL BE BACK IN THE MARKET SOON...

TAP TAP

RING RING

IT'S CLIVE... SHOULD I PICK UP?

NOT YET...

FLASH

...NOT TILL I'VE FINISHED PITCHING FOR YOUR ACCOUNT...

Alex PEATTIE + TAYLOR

SO HAS BRIDGET FOUND OUT THAT YOU WERE SACKED FROM YOUR JOB AT THE BANK YET, CLIVE?

SHH... NO...

WELL, I'M AFRAID THE NEWS IS ALL OVER THE SOCIAL CIRCLES THAT WE MOVE IN... IT'S ONLY A MATTER OF TIME UNTIL IT'LL BE BROUGHT TO HER ATTENTION...

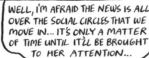

OH GOD. DO YOU THINK SO?

NO DOUBT ABOUT IT, CLIVE... IT'S FRANKLY JUST A QUESTION OF HOW MANY PEOPLE SHE FINDS HERSELF RUBBING SHOULDERS WITH ON SOCIAL OCCASIONS LIKE THIS...

THIS IS ODD... WHY HAS NO ONE TURNED UP?

WELL IT WAS NICE OF _YOU_ TO COME TO MY BARBECUE, ALEX...

I'VE NO REASON NOT TO... THERE'D BE NO POINT IN YOUR BEGGING _ME_ TO GET YOU A JOB WHERE I WORK...

Alex PEATTIE + TAYLOR

TYPICAL! AS SOON AS THERE'S A DOWNTURN IN THE ECONOMIC CYCLE I GET FIRED... THAT'S HOW AMERICAN BANKS THINK, CLIVE...

BUT THERE'S STILL HOPE FOR YOU... YOU MIGHT GET A JOB AT A EUROPEAN OR ASIAN BANK... THEY HAVE A DIFFERENT MINDSET AND SEE THIS AS AN OPPORTUNITY TO PICK UP GOOD PEOPLE...

YOU MEAN THEY HAVE A BUSINESS STRATEGY THAT ENCOMPASSES A LONGER-TERM VISION AND INVOLVES A GENUINE COMMITMENT TO THEIR EMPLOYEES?

EXACTLY, CLIVE...

AND BY THE TIME THEY REALISE HOW FUTILE THAT IS AND GET ROUND TO FIRING YOU, THE AMERICAN BANKS MIGHT BE RECRUITING AGAIN.

Alex PEATTIE + TAYLOR

HELLO, SHELLEY. KEEPING BUSY? I'M ONE OF THE PEOPLE YOU MADE REDUNDANT LAST WEEK...

OH YES... I'M SO SORRY ABOUT THAT...

YEAH RIGHT. I EXPECT IT'S REALLY EMOTIONALLY STRESSFUL FOR YOU H.R. PEOPLE; PUTTING PEOPLE OUT OF WORK... I BET THE PROSPECT OF MORE MANAGEMENT CUTS REALLY BREAKS YOUR DELICATE LITTLE HEARTS...

WITHERING SARCASM...

IT DOES ACTUALLY... WE GET REALLY UPSET ABOUT IT.

I DON'T SEE _YOU_ SHEDDING MANY TEARS TODAY...

WELL I WILL BE IN PRIVATE I CAN ASSURE YOU...

I'M GLAD TO HEAR IT...

WE'RE GOING TO NEED TO SHED A FEW MORE TIERS, SHELLEY...

RIGHTY-HO... I'VE GOT A JUMBO PACK OF BIN LINERS. LEAVE IT TO ME...

MEGABANK MANAGEMENT STRUCTURE

Alex PEATTIE + TAYLOR

POOR CLIVE'S LOST HIS JOB AND WHO KNOWS WHICH ONE OF US COULD BE NEXT FOR THE CHOP?

IT'S SCARY...

AND _SO_ FRUSTRATING... EXPERIENCED BANKERS LIKE US SITTING AROUND IDLY, UNABLE TO PUT THE PROFESSIONAL SKILLS WE'VE ACQUIRED OVER A CAREER IN THE CITY TO USE...

IT'S ALL THANKS TO THIS BLASTED SUB-PRIME CRISIS, WHICH HAS UNDERMINED THE VERY BASIS ON WHICH THE WHOLE BANKING SYSTEM FUNCTIONS... I'M TALKING ABOUT _CREDIT_...

WHAT, _TAKING_ IT FOR OTHER PEOPLE'S DEALS?

EXACTLY. BUT HOW CAN ONE DO THAT WHEN NO-ONE'S _GOT_ ANY DEALS?

Alex PEATTIE + TAYLOR

I THINK THE SHEER SPEED OF THE LEHMAN BROTHERS COLLAPSE HAS TAKEN EVERYONE BY SURPRISE...

ONLY LAST WEEK THOSE GUYS WERE MASTERS OF THE UNIVERSE SITTING IN BIG OFFICES IMPLEMENTING SOME GRANDIOSE MISSION STATEMENT.

"WHERE VISION GETS BUILT" WAS THEIRS.

SO HOW WILL THEY REACT TO SOMETHING LIKE THIS: FINDING THEMSELVES SUDDENLY DROWNING THEIR SORROWS HERE IN THIS WINE BAR WITH US?

AH YES.

SO THEY HAVEN'T STOPPED OUR CORPORATE CREDIT CARDS YET? GOOD..

"WHERE DOUBLE VISION GETS BUILT..."

TWO MORE MAGNUMS OF KRUG

Alex PEATTIE + TAYLOR

SO BRIDGET STILL HASN'T REALISED YOU'VE BEEN FIRED, CLIVE?

NO.

WELL, I'VE BEEN GETTING UP EACH MORNING AND GOING INTO THE CITY AS IF I STILL HAD A JOB... BUT I DON'T KNOW HOW MUCH LONGER I CAN BLUFF HER FOR...

SHE'S BEEN VERY AGITATED OF LATE. SHE CLEARLY KNOWS THAT SOMETHING'S WRONG... IT'S BEEN AFFECTING HER SLEEPING AT NIGHT...

ANOTHER UNINTERRUPTED NIGHT...? HOW COME THAT AMERICAN BOSS OF YOURS DOESN'T PHONE YOU AT ALL HOURS ANY MORE...?

ER...

BZZZ...

Alex PEATTIE + TAYLOR

Strip 1

DURING A BULL MARKET BANKS INEVITABLY GET FLABBY THROUGH OVER-RECRUITING, ESPECIALLY IN THE MIDDLE OFFICE...

ALL THOSE CORPORATE COMMS, MARKETING AND H.R. PEOPLE HAVE NO DEMONSTRABLE VALUE, WHEREAS THE BANKERS LIKE US ACTUALLY GENERATE INCOME IN THE FORM OF FEES...

SO NOW THE ECONOMY'S SLIPPING INTO RECESSION IT'S OBVIOUS WHO'S FIRST IN LINE TO GET THE SACK...
YES...

THE BANKERS, LIKE POOR CLIVE THERE, AS HE WAS DEMONSTRABLY BRINGING IN NO REVENUE...
WHEREAS THE VALUE OF THOSE MIDDLE OFFICE PEOPLE IS STILL UNDETERMINABLE.

Strip 2

IT'S AS IF THE WHOLE FINANCIAL WORLD HAS GONE MAD... THERE'S PANIC OUT THERE AND NAKED FEAR...

EVERYONE'S TERRIFIED THAT THE WHOLE BANKING SYSTEM COULD COLLAPSE... NO-ONE BENEFITS FROM THIS... WE ALL GET HURT...
NOT ME... I'M DOING ALRIGHT OUT OF IT...

WHAT? YOU'RE ONE OF THE PEOPLE WHO'S BEEN MAKING A PROFIT FROM THE CURRENT SITUATION? YOU'RE A SHORT-SELLER?
THAT'S RIGHT.

BOXER SHORTS! FRESH BOXER SHORTS!
GIVE ME 3 PAIRS... IT LOOKS LIKE ANOTHER SCARY DAY
I NEED SOME FOR MY WHOLE DEPARTMENT.
OH GOD... I NEED A PAIR RIGHT NOW.

Strip 3

SO WHAT'S YOUR FEELING ABOUT THIS WEEK, ALEX? WILL WE BE SEEING MORE MARKET TURMOIL?
HOPEFULLY NOT, CYRUS

THE WILD DAILY SWINGS OF LAST WEEK WERE CAUSED BY MASS PANIC IN RESPONSE TO THE UNFOLDING ECONOMIC DATA. BUT WE'VE NOW HAD TIME FOR MATURE REFLECTION ON THE SITUATION...

I SUSPECT THE WISER HEADS AMONG US WILL HAVE IDENTIFIED THE ROOT CAUSES OF THE PROBLEM AND WILL NOW BE ABLE TO TAKE APPROPRIATE ACTION TO QUELL THE UNDERLYING VOLATILITY...

CLEARLY NO ONE HAS A CLUE WHAT'S GOING ON OR WHAT TO DO ABOUT IT, SO BEST JUST TO SWITCH THE BLACKBERRY OFF AND ENJOY A DECENT LUNCH...
VERY WISE...

Strip 4

WITH THE GLOBAL ECONOMY STILL SLOWING DOWN, OBVIOUSLY THE BANK NEEDS TO REIN IN EXPENDITURE...

YET IT'S DECIDED TO FLY US - ITS SENIOR DIRECTORS - FIRST CLASS FROM ALL OVER THE WORLD TO THIS 5-STAR HOTEL FOR A 3-DAY OFF-SITE TO DISCUSS COST-CUTTING...
AND YOUR POINT IS...?

WELL, WAS NO THOUGHT GIVEN BEFORE ALL THIS WAS ORGANISED? IN TIMES OF RECESSION ECONOMY MEASURES NEED TO BE ADOPTED BY EVERYONE, INCLUDING SENIOR PEOPLE LIKE US...
WE'RE AWARE OF THAT, DAVID.

WHICH IS WHY WE FIGURED WE COULD ALL USE SOME EXTRA AIR MILES...
RIGHT... WE STILL NEED TO BE ABLE TO TAKE OUR CHRISTMAS SKIING BREAKS...

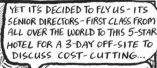

ALEX VENTURED OUTSIDE HIS COMFORT ZONE.

THE ALEX PLAY TOURED THE WORLD, THE U.K. AND CAME BACK TO LONDON.

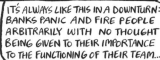

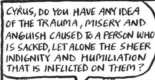

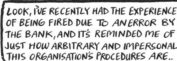

24

Strip 1

 **Alex** PEATTIE + TAYLOR — IT'S GOOD TO SEE THAT RESOLVING THE CREDIT CRISIS IS HELPING BRING TOGETHER PEOPLE OF DIFFERING IDEOLOGIES.

 FOR EXAMPLE, CYRUS, MY AMERICAN BOSS, IS A STAUNCH REPUBLICAN, WHEREAS NICK, WHO HE'S TALKING TO, IS A DYED-IN-THE-WOOL SOCIALIST...

 I THINK IT'S VERY IMPRESSIVE THAT DESPITE BEING FROM OPPOSING POLITICAL WINGS THEY'RE ABLE TO SEE EYE-TO-EYE AND AGREE ON THE CRUCIAL ISSUES OF THE MOMENT...

 NAMELY THAT EVERYTHING IS THE FAULT OF THEIR RESPECTIVE OPPOSITIONS... THE TORIES CAUSED ALL THIS BY DEREGULATING FINANCIAL MARKETS IN 1986... I BLAME THE DEMOCRATS FOR REPEALING THE GLASS-STEAGAL ACT IN 1999...

Strip 2

 **Alex** PEATTIE + TAYLOR — WITH THE MARKET FOR DEALS TOTALLY DEAD, WE DIRECTORS HAVE SOME TOUGH DECISIONS TO MAKE...

 SHOULD WE AUTHORISE EXPENDITURE ON THINGS LIKE BUSINESS TRIPS, SO OUR PEOPLE CAN FORGE NEW CLIENT RELATIONSHIPS AND CEMENT EXISTING ONES..?

 OR SHOULD WE ACCEPT THAT THERE'S NO BUSINESS OUT THERE, CUT COSTS TO THE BONE AND CONSERVE OUR RESOURCES TILL THE MARKET PICKS UP AGAIN? IT'S A TRICKY ONE...

 SO, IS IT BETTER FOR US TO BE SEEN BY MANAGEMENT TO BE AT OUR DESKS AND WORKING HARD...? OR TO BE OFF ON A BUSINESS TRIP AND HOPEFULLY GET OVER-LOOKED WHEN THE NEXT REDUNDANCIES HAPPEN? HMM...IT'S A TRICKY ONE...

Strip 3

Alex PEATTIE + TAYLOR — AT TIMES LIKE THIS ONE HAS TO QUESTION THE WISDOM OF THE GOVERNMENT AND THE BANK OF ENGLAND...

 THEY KEEP REPEATING THE SAME MANTRA: THAT CITY BONUSES MUST BE REINED IN AND THAT THE U.K. IS HEADING FOR A SEVERE RECESSION IN 2009...

 BUT CAN'T THEY SEE THE INEVITABLE CONSEQUENCES OF THESE CONTINUED PESSIMISTIC PRONOUNCEMENTS ABOUT THE BRITISH ECONOMY...?

 THAT THE POUND COLLAPSES AND THOSE OF US WHO WORK FOR U.S. BANKS AND GET PAID IN DOLLARS SEE THE VALUE OF OUR BONUSES GO UP..? QUITE... SO KEEP SPREADING THE GLOOM, MERVYN... STERLING v DOLLAR

Strip 4

 **Alex** PEATTIE + TAYLOR — ONLY 17 MEMBERS OF YOUR DEPARTMENT HAVE COMPLETED AND RETURNED THEIR ANNUAL APPRAISAL FORMS...

 LOOK, WITH ALL DUE RESPECT TO YOUR ROLE AS H.R. DIRECTOR, SHELLEY, MY PEOPLE HAVE BEEN EXTREMELY BUSY FIGHTING A GLOBAL FINANCIAL CRISIS... I'M AWARE OF THAT...

 BUT DUE TO THAT CRISIS YOU WILL HAVE LESS MONEY TO SHARE AMONG YOUR DEPARTMENT AT THE END OF THE YEAR...THIS IS WHERE APPRAISALS CAN GUIDE YOU IN MAKING THE NECESSARY DECISIONS... YES... I TAKE YOUR POINT.

 SO GIVE ME THE NAMES OF THE 17 GUYS WHO RECKONED THEY HAD THE TIME TO FILL IN THIS RUBBISH AND I'LL FIRE THEM IMMEDIATELY...

Alex PEATTIE + TAYLOR

So your bank took the government's bail-out and is now semi-nationalised, Neil?

Yes.

But in many ways it's a good thing, Alex. Obviously we're having to cut costs but we're also being more socially responsible in how we spend money.

We're more conscious of our obligations to the ordinary taxpayer and the need to invest in organisations that directly benefit the nation's stakeholders...

He's putting a brave face on his bank's new travel policy...

PUBLIC TRANSPORT? EE-EEW...

TAXI!

UNDERGROUND STATION

Alex PEATTIE + TAYLOR

I got a call from Robin Thorne today.

Our ex-graduate trainee? How's his hedge fund doing?

It went bust last week. He was sounding me out about possible job openings here...

Well, sadly for him we've got a total hiring freeze on...

That's true, Clive, but we did a lot of business with his hedge fund in the good times, so I think it's only fair to get him in for an interview now...

Right. You've got 30 seconds. Give me your best three investment ideas... then get out...

MEETING ROOM

ALEX IS ENJOYING TREATING _HIM_ LIKE HE USED TO TREAT _US_...

Alex PEATTIE + TAYLOR

I've noticed it's rare these days for people to put their date of birth on their C.V., Shelley...

HEAD OF H.R.

It's no longer obligatory, Alex. Employers are now prohibited from making adverse judgements about a candidate on grounds of their age...

This system works particularly in favour of _your_ generation Alex, - the over-40's...it provides you with a certain degree of protection...

OH MY GOD...

This candidate was born in the 1990's... how laughable... and at the same time rather scary...

...from saying things like _that_ when you're interviewing for a new P.A....

C.V.

Alex PEATTIE + TAYLOR

So your bank has spurned the British government's offer of rescue?

IT'S JUST PRAGMATIC THINKING, ALEX...

The credit crisis is redrawing the geography of the business world. Finance-based economies like the U.K. could be losing their international influence.

Which is why we decided to sell ourselves to the Middle East... with their commodity-derived wealth they are able to offer a more useful, competitive business perspective...

Their C.E.O. is on £20m a year? That sounds very reasonable...

I mean, that's what _I_ earn in a week from my family's oil wells...

27

"ALEX" RAN FOR FOUR WEEKS IN LONDON

Alex PEATTIE + TAYLOR

HMM... I SUSPECT THAT YOU MAY BE SUFFERING FROM STRESS...

ME? NO, I DON'T THINK SO...

MANY OF YOU HIGH-FLYING FINANCIAL TYPES, OUTWARDLY CONFIDENT, SECRETLY FEAR LOSING YOUR JOBS AND THE INEVITABLE HARDSHIP IT WOULD BRING...

NOT ME... I'M NOT WORRIED...

IT CAN MANIFEST ITSELF IN MANY WAYS: INSOMNIA, IRRITABLE BOWEL SYNDROME, FATIGUE... OR INDEED THE SYMPTOMS YOU'RE REPORTING.

WHAT, A LONG-TERM ANKLE NIGGLE FROM PLAYING CRICKET?

YES. THE FACT THAT YOU WANT IT OPERATED ON *NOW* SHOWS THAT YOU DON'T THINK YOU'LL HAVE AN EMPLOYER TO FUND THE PRIVATE MEDICAL INSURANCE FOR MUCH LONGER.

LOOK IF I WANTED ANALYSIS I'D HAVE GONE TO A THERAPIST...

Alex PEATTIE + TAYLOR

THE GOVERNMENT IS DESPERATE TO CLAW ITS WAY OUT OF THIS ECONOMIC CRISIS, CLIVE...

BUT THE OFFICIAL STATISTICS OFTEN DON'T EVEN KEEP UP WITH THE LATEST EVENTS... MUCH OF THE DATA FAILS TO REFLECT THE DIRENESS OF THE SITUATION...

FOR EXAMPLE, WHEN YOU'RE THINKING ABOUT THE JOBLESS FIGURES, YOU NEED TO BE AWARE OF WHICH ONES ARE LAGGING...

AH, YES OF COURSE...

THE PEOPLE ON NEW "GREEN", ENERGY-SAVING GOVERNMENT JOB CREATION SCHEMES, BEING SENT TO <u>INSULATE OUR ATTICS</u>...

ACTUALLY THEY'RE LOOKING FOR WHERE PEOPLE HAVE STASHED THEIR SAVINGS, CLIVE.

EEK!

Alex PEATTIE + TAYLOR

I BLAME THE REGULATORS FOR THE CREDIT CRUNCH —FOR NOT IMPOSING STRICTER FINANCIAL CONTROLS...

YES, AND CONSUMERS MUST BE HELD RESPONSIBLE TOO, FOR LIVING BEYOND THEIR MEANS ON CREDIT CARD LOANS AND BUYING PROPERTIES THEY COULDN'T AFFORD...

HOLD ON...

THESE ARE THE SAME CONSUMERS WHO, AS TAXPAYERS, HAVE HAD TO BAIL OUT THE BANKS. WHEN SEARCHING FOR WHO TO BLAME, DOES IT NOT OCCUR TO YOU THAT *WE* MIGHT FALL INTO THAT CATEGORY?

DON'T BE SILLY, CLIVE...

<u>I</u> DON'T PAY U.K. TAX...

NO... ME NEITHER... WHY?... DO <u>YOU</u>...?

Alex PEATTIE + TAYLOR

WELL, AT LEAST WE SEEM TO HAVE SURVIVED THE LATEST REDUNDANCIES...

MAYBE, BUT THE OUTLOOK IS STILL GRIM, CLIVE...

I HATE IT WHEN THE BANK'S DIRECTORS GET INTO THIS PETTY, OBSESSIVE MINDSET WHERE CUTTING COSTS IS THEIR ONLY OBJECTIVE. THE CHRISTMAS PARTY HAS BEEN THE LATEST VICTIM...

I SUPPOSE WE SHOULD FOCUS ON THE GOOD NEWS, ALEX... AT LEAST ALL EMPLOYEES ARE TO BE GIVEN £10 TO ORGANISE OUR OWN CELEBRATIONS.

YOU THINK THAT'S GOOD NEWS, CLIVE?

SO, FOR ANYONE ELSE WE NOW SACK BEFORE CHRISTMAS THE BANK WILL SAVE AN EXTRA £10...

RIGHT... LET'S TAKE ANOTHER LOOK AT THAT HEADCOUNT REDUCTION LIST...

Alex
PEATTIE + TAYLOR

Strip 1:

Panel 1: BUSINESS LEVELS HAVE BEEN DISASTROUS FOR ALL BANKS OVER THE LAST SIX MONTHS, THANKS TO THE CREDIT CRUNCH...

Panel 2: ON THE OTHER HAND IT DID GIVE US THE OPPORTUNITY TO TAKE OVER ONE OF OUR MAJOR COMPETITORS ON THE CHEAP AND PICK UP SOME EXTREMELY ABLE PEOPLE IN THE PROCESS...

Panel 3: AS THE INTEGRATION PROCESS PROCEEDS ONE CAN ALREADY SEE THE EFFECT ON OUR PRODUCTIVITY AS REFLECTED IN OUR LATEST MONTHLY BUSINESS FIGURES... YES...

Panel 4: THEY'RE UTTERLY DISMAL... WELL, EVERYONE'S TOO BUSY LOBBYING FOR THEIR JOBS AND BACK-STABBING THEIR COLLEAGUES TO DO ANY ACTUAL WORK...

Strip 2:

Panel 1: MEGABANK HAS ANNOUNCED THAT WE BOARD DIRECTORS WILL NOT BE RECEIVING BONUSES THIS YEAR...

Panel 2: THIS IS A PUBLIC GESTURE TO TRY TO REGAIN THE RESPECT AND CREDIBILITY THAT SENIOR BANKERS HAVE LOST AS A RESULT OF THE CREDIT CRUNCH.

Panel 3: AFTER ALL, FOR MANY YEARS WE HAVE BEEN AWARDING OURSELVES ASTRONOMICAL BONUSES THAT WOULD BE OBSCENE IN MOST PEOPLE'S EYES... YES...

Panel 4: ...AND CLAIMING SUCH PAYMENTS WERE ESSENTIAL IF THE BANK IS TO RETAIN OUR "TALENT" AND PREVENT US FROM BEING POACHED BY COMPETITORS... I'M JUST HOPING A HEADHUNTER WILL CALL SOON OR THIS COULD BE EMBARRASSING...

Strip 3:

Panel 1: THE ONLY GOOD THING ABOUT THE CREDIT CRUNCH IS THAT LOADS OF HEDGE FUNDS HAVE GONE BUST... THAT'S TRUE.

Panel 2: WHILE THEY WERE MAKING MILLIONS THEY USED TO LORD IT OVER US BORING BANKERS WHO STAYED IN OUR SAFE JOBS AND DIDN'T HAVE THE COURAGE TO START OUR OWN BUSINESSES...

Panel 3: IT'S A CLEAR CASE OF PRIDE GOING BEFORE A FALL, CLIVE. AND NOW THEY'VE ALL BEEN WIPED OUT I THINK WE CAN BASK IN A JUSTIFIABLE SENSE OF SUPERIORITY... QUITE.

Panel 4: AT LEAST WE WEREN'T STUPID ENOUGH TO INVEST OUR OWN MONEY IN ALL THAT TOXIC RUBBISH... NO... JUST OUR CLIENTS'

Strip 4:

Panel 1: I NEVER THOUGHT THE CREDIT CRISIS WOULD EVER MAKE ME QUESTION MY OWN VALUES, PENNY... UNTIL NOW...

Panel 2: I ONLY EVER CARED ABOUT MYSELF BEFORE... NEVER ABOUT OTHERS...I TOOK SO MUCH FOR GRANTED... BUT NOW I FEEL QUITE UNCOMFORTABLE COMING OUT FOR AN EXTRAVAGANT EVENING LIKE THIS... IT FEELS WRONG...

Panel 3: I MEAN, HOW CAN I REALLY ENJOY A LAVISH MEAL IN A SWANKY RESTAURANT, KNOWING THAT EVERY-ONE I KNOW IS EITHER SUDDENLY IMPOVERISHED OR SCARED SICK OF LOSING THEIR LIVELIHOOD..?

Panel 4: IF THEY AREN'T GOING OUT, NO-ONE WILL EVEN SEE ME HERE... FROM A PHILOSOPHICAL POINT OF VIEW, DO I EVEN EXIST? THERE, THERE...

Alex PEATTIE + TAYLOR

Strip 1

ALEX, ARE YOU REALLY SURE WE CAN AFFORD TO EAT IN THIS EXPENSIVE RESTAURANT THESE DAYS?

OF COURSE, PENNY...

AND THAT LUXURY SKI-ING HOLIDAY YOU'VE JUST BOOKED..? I MEAN, SHOULDN'T WE BE CUTTING BACK? AFTER ALL, THE COUNTRY IS HEADING FOR RECESSION...

YES...

AND IN ORDER TO AVOID A RECESSION, PENNY, CONSUMERS NEED TO SPEND, WHICH IS PRECISELY WHAT WE'RE DOING...

BUT ARE YOU SURE YOU'RE NOT OVER-REACTING, ALEX?

THOSE NEWSPAPER REPORTS THAT BANKS ARE CONSULTING LAWYERS ABOUT CLAWING BACK PEOPLE'S LAST YEAR'S BONUSES MIGHT NOT BE TRUE...

WELL, LET'S JUST MAKE SURE THERE'S NOTHING FOR THEM TO CLAW BACK...

YOUR MOUTON ROTHSCHILD '82, SIR...

Strip 2

PEOPLE WERE JUST BORROWING MONEY AND GAMBLING ON EVERYTHING GOING UP: STOCKS, COMMODITIES, HOUSE PRICES...

BUT IT'S A ZERO SUM GAME: WHAT GOES UP MUST COME DOWN; AND THE DOWNSIDE IS VERY PAINFUL...

ABSOLUTELY...IT WAS MADNESS; UTTERLY RECKLESS BEHAVIOUR.

HOPEFULLY PEOPLE WILL NOW START THINKING IN THE LONG TERM AND SAVING ... AFTER ALL THERE ARE ADVANTAGES TO BEING RESPONSIBLE. YOU GET 40% TAX RELIEF ON MONEY INVESTED IN A PENSION SCHEME...

TRUE...

AND HOW MUCH HAS THE STOCK MARKET - WHICH THE PENSION FUNDS ARE INVESTED IN - GONE DOWN BY THIS YEAR?

ER... ABOUT 40%...

AS I SAY, CLIVE, IT'S A ZERO SUM GAME...

Strip 3

≡SIGH≡ NO ONE GOES OUT TO LUNCH ANY MORE. PEOPLE JUST SPEND ALL DAY AT THEIR DESKS...

LUNCH USED TO BE THE LIFEBLOOD OF THE CITY - A FORUM FOR CONVERSATION, ANALYSIS, INFORMAL EXCHANGE OF OPINIONS AND IDEAS...

THESE DAYS WE HAVE BLOGS FOR THAT, ALEX...

BLOGS?!! CONSISTING OF ILL-INFORMED GOSSIP, RANDOM DRIVEL, INCONSEQUENTIAL PONTIFICATIONS.?

AND HOW'S THAT SO DIFFERENT FROM WHAT YOU USED TO TALK ABOUT AT LUNCH?

WELL, THE CLIENT IS SOBER WHEN HE'S APPRISED OF IT; SO YOU CAN'T GET HIM TO DO DEALS ON THE BASIS OF IT WHEN HE GETS BACK TO HIS OFFICE AND IS STILL SQUIFFY...

UNLIKE WITH A LUNCH...

YES, YES... I GET YOUR POINT...

Strip 4

THE EXTENT OF THE PENNY-PINCHING IN THE CITY HAS NOW BECOME RIDICULOUS...

DO YOU KNOW THAT OUR BANK IS NOW CHARGING EMPLOYEES FOR REPLACING LOST OR DAMAGED SECURITY PASSES?

IT'S SHOCKING, I AGREE...

CLIVE WAS JUST PHONED UP BY SOME FUNCTIONARY FROM THE PREMISES DEPARTMENT AND TOLD HE HAD TO PAY £15 TO HAVE HIS DEFECTIVE PASS REPLACED...YOU CAN IMAGINE HIS REACTION...

UTTER DELIGHT, CLEARLY.

QUITE...WHEN IT STOPPED WORKING YESTERDAY HE WAS CONVINCED HE'D BEEN FIRED...

THANK YOU, THANK YOU, THANK YOU... WHO DO I MAKE THE CHEQUE OUT TO?

alex@alexcartoon.com

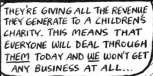

ALEX IS RESTING

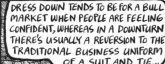

Strip 1

WELL, IT'S 2009, PENNY: MY FIRST DAY BACK AT WORK AND I'M WONDERING WHAT TO WEAR...

DRESS DOWN TENDS TO BE FOR A BULL MARKET WHEN PEOPLE ARE FEELING CONFIDENT, WHEREAS IN A DOWNTURN THERE'S USUALLY A REVERSION TO THE TRADITIONAL BUSINESS UNIFORM OF A SUIT AND TIE...

IT'S A QUESTION OF HOW ONE GAUGES THE NEW MOOD AND WHAT STATEMENT ONE WANTS TO MAKE... SO I THINK I SHALL OPT FOR MY CASUAL WARDROBE...

BECAUSE YOU'RE FEELING BULLISH?

ER... NO... BECAUSE I DON'T WANT TO LOOK LIKE A BANKER IN PUBLIC... WE'RE NOT EXACTLY THE MOST POPULAR PEOPLE AROUND RIGHT NOW...

Strip 2

LISTEN TO ALEX RANTING ON ABOUT RAIL FARE INCREASES

IT'S AN OUTRAGE...

WELL, IT'S A STANDARD MANTRA IN JANUARY...

THOUGH I SUPPOSE WHAT HE'S TALKING ABOUT IS MORE RELEVANT THAN EVER WHEN YOU CONSIDER THAT WE'RE IN A RECESSIONARY AND DEFLATIONARY ENVIRONMENT...

MY SEASON TICKET'S GONE UP TO £3,200...

SO UNDER THE CIRCUMSTANCES IT'S UNDERSTANDABLE THAT THIS IS A MATTER HE'D WANT TO DRAW TO PEOPLE'S ATTENTION...

EXCESSIVE PROFITEERING BY THE TRAIN COMPANIES?

NO, THE FACT THAT HE'S CONFIDENT ENOUGH OF HIS EMPLOYMENT PROSPECTS THIS YEAR TO HAVE BOUGHT A FULL ANNUAL SEASON TICKET...

OH GOD... I CAN'T SAY I DID...

GLOOM

NO... ME NEITHER.

Strip 3

THE BANK FIRED MOST OF LAST SUMMER'S GRADUATE INTAKE IN THE LATEST ROUND OF REDUNDANCIES...

SO THEIR BRIEF FLIRTATION WITH INVESTMENT BANKING IS OVER... WE ENCOURAGED THEM TO BUY INTO THE CORPORATE DREAM AND THEN KICKED THEM OUT AT THE FIRST HURDLE...

THEY SHOULD HAVE KNOWN THAT OURS IS A MERCILESS INDUSTRY, CLIVE. IN TOUGH TIMES LIKE THIS THE BANK HAS TO CLAW BACK MONEY IN EVERY WAY IT CAN...

YES...

SO WE'RE MAKING THEM PAY BACK THE £10,000 LOANS WE GAVE THEM SO THEY'D BE ABLE TO PURCHASE MEGABANK STOCK... WHICH HAS NOW QUARTERED IN VALUE... IT SERVES THEM RIGHT FOR BEING SO PATHETICALLY LOYAL...

Strip 4

THE ONE THING WE CAN CONFIDENTLY PREDICT ABOUT 2009 IS THAT THERE WILL BE A HUGE RISE IN FINANCIAL REGULATION...

THANKS TO THE SUBPRIME CRISIS AND THE CREDIT CRUNCH, WE BANKERS HAVE BEEN EXPOSED AS BEING NAIVE, IGNORANT, RECKLESS AND SHORT-SIGHTED IN OUR APPROACH TO RISK-TAKING.

SO, AS COST-CUTTING INTENSIFIES, THE BANK WILL BE RECRUITING EVEN MORE COMPLIANCE PEOPLE, AT THE SAME TIME AS IT'S FIRING CRUCIAL MEMBERS OF OUR TEAM...

YES...

SUCH AS OUR GRADUATE TRAINEE WHO WE USED TO GET TO TAKE ALL THE ON-LINE REGULATORY TESTS FOR US...

OH GAWD. WE MAY ACTUALLY HAVE TO DO THEM OURSELVES THIS YEAR...

Row 1:

IN RETROSPECT EMPLOYING YOU BRAND MANAGEMENT CONSULTANTS WAS A CLASSIC PIECE OF BULL MARKET FOLLY.

THE BANK SPENT MILLIONS HAVING YOU REDESIGN OUR CORPORATE LOGO: MONEY THAT COULD BETTER HAVE BEEN INVESTED IN SOME SENSIBLE COMPLIANCE PROCEDURES TO AVERT FINANCIAL DISASTER...

BUT, RUPERT,...

YOU DON'T UNDERSTAND: DURING A RECESSION IS EXACTLY THE TIME THE BANK NEEDS TO RESTORE CUSTOMER CONFIDENCE BY PROJECTING A STRONG BRAND IDENTITY...

EXACTLY...

BUT WE'VE GOT RID OF SO MANY PEOPLE THAT WE NOW OCCUPY LESS THAT 50% OF OUR BUILDING, SO WE'RE NO LONGER ALLOWED TO DISPLAY OUR LOGO ON THE ROOFTOP...

YOU'RE FIRED.

Row 2:

JUST LOOK AT THIS JOB APPLICATION FROM SOME 23-YEAR-OLD GRADUATE...

THE ARROGANCE OF THESE KIDS... SHE SAYS SHE HAS "IN-DEPTH EXPERIENCE OF INVESTMENT BANKING..." BECAUSE SHE DID A SUMMER INTERNSHIP 2 YEARS AGO... HOW LAUGHABLE!

I MEAN INTERNS JUST SIT AROUND SURFING THE INTERNET, E-MAILING THEIR FRIENDS AND INVENTING OTHER POINTLESS TASKS TO WHILE AWAY THE HOURS...

ER...

GET HER IN... SOUNDS LIKE SHE'S GOT THE MEASURE OF WHAT THE JOB INVOLVES IN THE CURRENT MARKET...

A SHAME WE'RE NOT ACTUALLY HIRING...

Row 3:

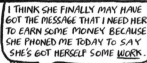

WITH BONUSES LOOKING NON-EXISTENT THIS YEAR, WE BANKERS ARE GOING TO FIND OURSELVES SERIOUSLY FINANCIALLY STRAPPED.

OF COURSE OUR WIVES JUST SHOP AND LUNCH AND EXPECT US TO FUND IT... WELL I'VE BEEN DROPPING HINTS TO MINE THAT THINGS ARE GOING TO BE ECONOMICALLY TOUGH FOR EVERYONE THIS YEAR...

I THINK SHE FINALLY MAY HAVE GOT THE MESSAGE THAT I NEED HER TO EARN SOME MONEY BECAUSE SHE PHONED ME TODAY TO SAY SHE'S GOT HERSELF SOME WORK.

ER...SO YOU'RE WORKING ON A CHARITY COMMITTEE?

YES, DARLING: TO RAISE MONEY FOR THE HOMELESS...SO I'LL NEED YOU TO TAKE A TABLE AT THE BALL... IT'S ONLY £3,000...

Row 4:

THE BANK NEEDS TO CUT COSTS, CLIVE, SO WE'VE BEEN GOING THROUGH PEOPLE'S ITEMIZED CELL PHONE BILLS.

WE HAVE A DEDICATED TEAM WHO VERIFY ALL THE NUMBERS YOU'VE DIALED TO BE CERTAIN YOUR CALLS ARE FOR LEGITIMATE AND ACCEPTABLE BUSINESS PURPOSES...

I'M HAPPY TO INFORM YOU THAT YOUR NUMBERS CHECK OUT. YOUR PHONE USE IS 100% BONA FIDE, CLIVE. KEEP UP THE GOOD WORK.

ER, THANKS, CYRUS...

BUT AT LEAST HALF THE PEOPLE I'M CALLING ARE HEADHUNTERS, TO STRENGTHEN MY BONUS-NEGOTIATING POSITION... WHAT'S CYRUS TRYING TO TELL ME?

WE'RE ALL EXPENDABLE IN THIS MARKET, CLIVE...

39

Alex
PEATTIE + TAYLOR

Strip 1

 AS THE NEW YEAR SETTLES IN, IT'S BECOMING VERY CLEAR HOW GRIM THINGS ARE ECONOMICALLY...

 YOU CAN SENSE RECESSION IN THE AIR JUST FROM THE DEMEANOUR OF PEOPLE ON THE STREET, FROM THEIR BODY LANGUAGE AND THE AURA THEY PROJECT...

 AS THE ECONOMIC DOWNTURN REALLY STARTS TO BE FELT IT HAS INEVITABLE EFFECTS ON PEOPLE'S HEALTH AND WELL-BEING...

YES

 NORMALLY EVERYONE HAS GIVEN UP ON THEIR NEW YEAR HEALTH KICK BY THE SECOND WEEK IN JANUARY...

BUT NO ONE'S GOT ANY DEALS ON AND THERE'S NO BUDGET FOR ANY LUNCHES...

GYM

HEALTHY GLOW

Alex
PEATTIE + TAYLOR

Strip 2

 I'VE ALWAYS THOUGHT THERE WAS A PARALLEL BETWEEN THE FINANCIAL WORLD AND THE ECOLOGY...

 AFTER ALL, THE CREDIT CRUNCH HAS COME ABOUT DUE TO PEOPLE BEING SELFISH, GREEDY AND THINKING IN THE SHORT TERM, JUST LIKE THE THREAT TO THE PLANET...

 NOW THAT THE LIKES OF ALEX ARE GOING TO HAVE TO START ADOPTING A LONGER TERM OUTLOOK FINANCIALLY IT SHOULD HOPEFULLY HAVE A CORRESPONDING EFFECT ON THEIR LEVEL OF ENVIRONMENTAL CONCERN...

I'M SURE IT WILL...

 WE'VE GOT TO BE ECONOMICALLY PRUDENT NOW, PENNY, SO WE CAN'T AFFORD TO WASTE MONEY ON FADDISH ORGANIC PRODUCE ANY MORE...

GREEN PLANET

HEALTH FOODS

ORGANIC PRODUCE

Alex
PEATTIE + TAYLOR

Strip 3

 DIVERSITY OF OPINION HAS ALWAYS BEEN A PRE-REQUISITE FOR THE EXISTENCE OF THE FINANCIAL WORLD...

  AFTER ALL IF EVERYONE AGREED ON EVERYTHING THERE'D BE NO MARKET. DIFFERENCES OF VIEWPOINT ARE GOOD BECAUSE THEY CREATE DIFFERENTIALS IN PRICES...

 THIS IN TURN LEADS TO ARBITRAGE OPPORTUNITIES WHICH CAN BE EXPLOITED BY PEOPLE LIKE US TO MAKE MONEY. THAT'S HOW THE SYSTEM HAS ALWAYS WORKED.

 THE BIG DANGER TO THE ECONOMY NOW IS DEFLATION...

ACTUALLY I THINK INFLATION IS THE REAL THREAT...

SO, ALEX, DOES IT MATTER THAT NO ONE CAN AGREE ON HOW TO GET OURSELVES OUT OF THE CURRENT MESS?

ER... LET'S HOPE NOT...

Alex
PEATTIE + TAYLOR

Strip 4

 THE TENDENCY OVER THE LAST 20 YEARS IN THE FINANCIAL MARKETS HAS BEEN TOWARDS INCREASED GLOBALISATION...

 BUT THIS IS NOW BEING BLAMED FOR EXACERBATING THE CURRENT CRISIS, WHEREBY PROBLEMS ENDEMIC TO ONE COUNTRY CAN QUICKLY INFECT THE ENTIRE WORLD ECONOMY...

 THE DANGER NOW IS OF CASH-STRAPPED BANKS PULLING IN THEIR HORNS AND RETREATING TO THEIR DOMESTIC ECONOMIES AND THUS FATALLY UNDERMINING THE FINANCIAL SYSTEM AS WE KNOW IT...

YES... IT'S SCARY...

 WHO'S GOING TO EMPLOY US WHEN WE GET FIRED BY MEGABANK?

QUITE. WE RELY ON THERE BEING SOME THIRD-RATE DUTCH OR AUSTRIAN BANK DESPERATE TO GET A FOOTHOLD IN THE LONDON MARKET.

alex@alexcartoon.com

Alex PEATTIE + TAYLOR

SO, RUMOURS ARE THAT THE GOVERNMENT IS SECRETLY SETTING UP A SO-CALLED "TOXIC" BANK?

THAT'S WHAT I'VE HEARD, CLIVE.

IT'D BE A DUMPING GROUND FOR ALL THE OTHER BANKS' SUB-PRIME DEBT. IT'S A LAST DITCH ATTEMPT TO FREE UP THE MARKETS AFTER PREVIOUS BAIL OUTS HAVE FAILED.

COULD IT WORK?

WELL, IT SEEMS A VERY USEFUL INITIATIVE TO ME. FRANKLY IT COULD BE JUST THE THING THAT THE FINANCIAL SECTOR NEEDS TO GET MONEY FLOWING AGAIN.

WHAT?! YOU'RE TELLING ME ANOTHER BANK WANTS TO HIRE YOU? DON'T TRY THAT TIRED OLD RUSE TO PRESSURIZE ME INTO GIVING YOU A BIGGER BONUS THIS YEAR, ALEX. NO ONE IS RECRUITING.

ON THE CONTRARY, CYRUS. I'VE HAD AN ATTRACTIVE OFFER FROM TOXIC BANK...

THE GOVERNMENT HAS SOUNDED ME OUT INFORMALLY ABOUT RUNNING THIS PROPOSED NEW "TOXIC BANK"...

OUR ROLE WOULD BE TO BUY UP ALL THE OTHER BANKS' SUB-PRIME DEBT. IT'S NOT A JOB ANY BANKER WOULD WANT ON HIS C.V. BUT I'M TOLD THERE'S A PEERAGE IN IT FOR ME...

OF COURSE IT WOULD BENEFIT MEGA-BANK: ALLOWING US TO REBUILD OUR FINANCES BY OFF-LOADING SOME OF THE LIABILITIES WE BROUGHT ONTO OUR BOOKS BACK IN THE BULL MARKET...

OUR SUB-PRIME DEBT?

NOT JUST THAT...

WHAT DO YOU MEAN: I'M BEING SECONDED TO WORK AT TOXIC BANK?

OR YOU COULD JUST RESIGN, CLIVE AND SAVE US A REDUNDANCY SETTLEMENT...

ZZZ

IT'S DIFFICULT TO SEE HOW THIS NEW "TOXIC" BANK I'VE BEEN SECONDED TO WORK FOR CAN HAVE ANY REAL FUNCTION AS A BANK...

TOXIC BANK

RECEPTION

ZZZ

AFTER ALL, EVERYONE KNOWS THAT THIS PLACE IS JUST A DUMPING GROUND FOR ALL THE BAD DEBT RESULTING FROM THE DISASTROUS LENDING POLICIES OF BANKS BACK IN THE BULL MARKET...

SO IN THE MINDS OF THE PUBLIC WE'RE ALREADY IRREDEEMABLY ASSOCIATED WITH INCOMPETENCE, MISMANAGEMENT, COCK-UP AND FAILURE...

HOLD ON... I'VE GOT IT...

SO WE'RE PITCHING TO BE SHIRT SPONSORS TO THE ENGLAND CRICKET TEAM?

WELL, WE HAVE THE PERFECT BRAND SYNERGY...

TOXIC BANK

BEING SECONDED TO THE GOVERNMENT'S TOXIC BANK IS NO EASY DEAL... I'M WORKING REALLY HARD...

ZZZ

WE'VE GOT TO BUY UP ALL THE SUBPRIME DEBT FROM THE OTHER BANKS. THE PROBLEM IS THEY ALL EXPECT US TO PAY TOP DOLLAR FOR THEIR WORTHLESS RUBBISH...

WELL, IT'S OUR ROLE TO MOP UP THAT STUFF...

YES, BUT WE'RE FUNDED BY PUBLIC MONEY... SURELY WE HAVE AN OBLIGATION TO TAKE ALL POSSIBLE STEPS TO MINIMISE THE COST OF THIS OPERATION TO THE TAX PAYER?

WE DO, CLIVE...

WHICH IS WHY YOUR ENTIRE BONUS THIS YEAR WILL BE PAYABLE IN TOXIC BANK STOCK...

OOH-ER...

Alex PEATTIE + TAYLOR

SO YOU'RE STILL ON SECONDMENT AT THE GOVERNMENT'S NEW TOXIC BANK, CLIVE?

YES,

ZZZ

OUR ROLE IS TO BUY UP ALL THE SUB-PRIME DEBT THE OTHER BANKS HAVE ON THEIR BOOKS... THE PROBLEM IS THAT IT'S EXTREMELY HARD TO PRICE SOME OF THESE COMPLEX FINANCIAL PRODUCTS...

BUT THANKS TO MY 20 YEARS' EXPERIENCE IN THE CITY I KNOW HOW TO GET THESE DEALS DONE AND I CAN TELL YOU : I DRIVE A PRETTY HARD BARGAIN...

SO : I'LL NEED YOU TO INVITE ME TO THE FRIDAY OF THE LORD'S TEST AND TAKE ME LAPDANCING AFTERWARDS....

AND FOR THAT YOU'LL BUY UP ALL OUR RUBBISH AT FULL BOOK VALUE?

IT'S A DEAL!

WELL, OF COURSE... IT'S NOT *MY* MONEY...

Alex PEATTIE + TAYLOR

WHAT DO YOU THINK OF THE GOVERNMENT'S SETTING UP A NEW INDEPENDENT REVIEW ON EXECUTIVE REMUNERATION?

GOVERNMENT TO ACT ON CITY BONUSES

I WELCOME IT...

IT'S IMPORTANT TO EXPLORE ALL THE OPTIONS. AN OBVIOUS SOLUTION IS FOR BONUSES TO BE DECIDED IN PRINCIPLE BUT ACTUAL PAYMENT OF THE MONEY TO BE DELAYED UNTIL THE BANK IS PROFITABLE AGAIN...

OBVIOUSLY IT'LL BE UP TO THE REVIEW COMMITTEE TO PRESENT ITS RECOMMEND-ATIONS ON HOW CITY BONUSES SHOULD BE PAID, BUT IT SEEMS ONLY SENSIBLE THAT THEY SHOULD BE DEFERRED...

THE BONUSES?

ER, NO... THE RECOMMENDATIONS: AS LONG AS POSSIBLE, SO WE BANKERS CAN SNAFFLE UP THE MONEY WHILE THERE'S STILL SOME LEFT...

WHICH IS WHY THIS YEAR - LONG REVIEW PROCESS IS PERFECT...

Alex PEATTIE + TAYLOR

IT'S INCREDIBLE; THE WAY VALUES HAVE SUDDENLY CHANGED NOW THE BOOM YEARS ARE OVER, VINCE...

MAKES ME QUITE NOSTALGIC FOR THE 80'S, ALEX...

YES, BUT THE PUBLIC WON'T PUT UP WITH THE KIND OF CULTURE OF BLATANT GREED THAT BECAME A WAY OF LIFE IN THE CITY...

NOT ANY MORE, NO...

YOU KNOW, I'VE HEARD A LOT OF TALK RECENTLY ABOUT BANKERS WAIVING THEIR BONUSES...

NOT SURPRISING IS IT?

CHEQUE WAVE

LOADSA MONEY!!

WINE BAR

BANK

WE'VE ALL DONE IT... THOSE WERE THE DAYS, EH? 1986...

Alex PEATTIE + TAYLOR

WELL THERE'S VERY LITTLE IN THE WAY OF GOOD NEWS IN THE FINANCIAL WORLD RIGHT NOW...

IN OUR HEART OF HEARTS I THINK ALL OF US KNOW THAT WE SCREWED UP BADLY AND WE'RE NOW FACING A DEEP AND PROLONGED ECONOMIC RECESSION...

AT THE MOMENT I'M SEEING NOTHING BUT GLOOM, MISERY, DESPONDENCY AND DISILLUSION-MENT ON THE FACES OF MY DEPARTMENT...

WHICH IS GREAT FOR *ME* BECAUSE FOR ONCE I KNOW YOU'RE NOT MERELY PUTTING IT ON TO SCAM ME INTO THINKING I HAD UNDERPAID YOUR BONUS...

I MIGHT BE, CYRUS.

NOT EVEN *YOU* WOULD EXPECT ANYTHING IN *THIS* CLIMATE, ALEX...

Alex — PEATTIE + TAYLOR

CYRUS CLAIMS THAT ANNOUNCING THIS YEAR'S BONUSES IS MUCH EASIER BECAUSE THERE'S NO PLAY-ACTING INVOLVED FROM US...

NORMALLY WE PRETEND TO BE DIS-APPOINTED AND SULLEN TO SUGGEST THAT HE DIDN'T PAY US ENOUGH, WHEREAS THIS YEAR NO ONE HAD ANY EXPECTATIONS OF GETTING ANYTHING AT ALL...

THAT'S TRUE...

≥SIGH≤ FOR ONCE WE DIDN'T HAVE TO BITE BACK OUR CHEEKS TO PREVENT OURSELVES FROM BURSTING INTO A GREAT BIG GRIN OF PURE DELIGHT WHEN TOLD THE AMOUNT...

SPEAK FOR YOURSELF, ALEX...

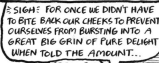

EH?

I WAS SO RELIEVED NOT TO BE FIRED THAT I WAS GENUINELY OVERJOYED WITH MY ZERO BONUS.

YES, BUT YOU REALLY ARE INCORRIGIBLY PATHETIC, CLIVE...

Alex — PEATTIE + TAYLOR

CYRUS HAS TOLD ME THAT DUE TO THE LACK OF BUSINESS I HAVE TO MAKE ONE MEMBER OF MY TEAM REDUNDANT...

SO YOU'D HAVE THE OPTION OF SENDING CHRISTIAN, OUR ANNOYING EUROTRASH JUNIOR PACKING BACK TO PARIS? THIS IS AN OPPORTUNITY FOR YOU TO GET YOUR REVENGE ON HIM.

AND ONE I INTEND TO TAKE, CLIVE...

JUST LOOKING AT HIM REMINDS ME OF EVERYTHING WE BRITS FIND INFURIATING ABOUT THE FRENCH: THEIR COMPLACENCY, THEIR SENSE OF CULTURAL SUPERIORITY, THEIR LAISSEZ-FAIRE ATTITUDE TO LIFE...

YES...

...AND THE HIGHLY INDULGENT WELFARE SYSTEM THEY HAVE OVER THERE WHEREBY THE UNEMPLOYED GET PAID 95% OF THEIR SALARY...

QUITE SO I'D RATHER KEEP HIM WORKING LONG HOURS HERE WITH NOTHING TO DO AND FIRE SOMEONE ELSE.

YAWN

Alex — PEATTIE + TAYLOR

THE RECESSION IS AFFECTING ALEX BADLY. INTERNATIONAL DEALS HAVE ALL BUT DRIED UP.

SO HE'S REDUCED TO SCHLEPPING ROUND THE U.K. TRYING TO DRUM UP BUSINESS FROM CLIENTS HERE, WHICH BRINGS ITS OWN PROBLEMS. HE HAD TO GO TO CARDIFF YESTERDAY...

REALLY?

WELL IT'S THE FIRST TIME HE'S HAD TO TRAVEL DOMESTICALLY FOR A WHILE SO HE'S HAVING A PREDICTABLE GRUMBLE ABOUT THE GENERAL STATE OF REPAIR AND EFFICIENCY OF THE RAILWAY SYSTEM HERE...

IT'S A DISGRACE.

THEY'VE UPGRADED THE BLASTED LINE AND THE JOURNEY TIME IS NOW UNDER 3 HOURS...

OH DEAR...MEANING THAT UNDER THE BANK'S TRAVEL POLICY YOU WEREN'T ALLOWED TO GO 1ST CLASS...

Alex — PEATTIE + TAYLOR

FUNNY TO THINK THAT SEVERAL OF OUR BANKS ARE NOW EFFECTIVELY OWNED BY THE GOVERNMENT. THEY'RE ODD BED-FELLOWS...

WELL, BOTH ARE TO BLAME FOR THE CREDIT CRISIS, CLIVE, WHICH WAS CAUSED BY THE IRRESPONSIBILITY AND GREED OF BANKERS, COUPLED WITH FAILINGS IN SUPERVISION AND REGULATION BY THE AUTHORITIES...

SO IN WORKING TOWARDS A FUNDAMENTAL FIX OF THE FLAWS IN OUR FINANCIAL SYSTEM, THESE 2 DISPARATE INDUSTRIES ARE NOW IDENTIFYING KEY AREAS OF COMMON GROUND AND SHARED METHODOLOGY...

SUCH AS AN INSTINCTIVE SHORT-TERMISM?

QUITE...THE BANKERS ARE LOOKING TO NEXT YEAR'S BONUS AND THE POLITICIANS AT NEXT YEAR'S ELECTION SO THEY'LL JUST PAPER OVER THE CRACKS TILL THEN.

Alex PEATTIE + TAYLOR

I SUPPOSE THIS GENERAL VILIFICATION OF BANKERS WAS PREDICTABLE...

AFTER ALL THE GOVERNMENT IS HAVING TO DEFEND ITS UNPOPULAR ACTIONS IN USING PUBLIC MONEY TO BAIL OUT THE BANKS' HUGE LOSSES ON COLLATERALISED DEBT...

SO IT'S AN OBVIOUS DIVERSIONARY PLOY TO FOCUS ON PORTRAYING US IN THE FINANCIAL COMMUNITY AS STUPID, INCOMPETENT AND SHORT-SIGHTED...

YES...

...FOR WANTING TO DUMP ALL OUR SUB-PRIME LIABILITIES... WHICH WE SHOULD BE TRYING TO HANG ONTO IF THE STUFF'S REALLY GOING TO BE VALUABLE ONE DAY, AS TAXPAYERS ARE BEING TOLD...

NEWS CITY FAT CATS

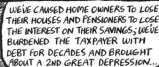

Alex PEATTIE + TAYLOR

THE LIST OF CRIMES BEING LAID AT THE DOOR OF OVERPAID BANKERS GETS LONGER EACH DAY...

WE'VE CAUSED HOME OWNERS TO LOSE THEIR HOUSES AND PENSIONERS TO LOSE THE INTEREST ON THEIR SAVINGS; WE'VE BURDENED THE TAXPAYER WITH DEBT FOR DECADES AND BROUGHT ABOUT A 2ND GREAT DEPRESSION...

YES INDEED...

AND NO DOUBT, AS WE SPEAK, NEW AND EVEN MORE SERIOUS CHARGES ARE BEING LEVELLED AGAINST US...

WHAT, MORE SERIOUS THAN DESTROYING THE ENTIRE GLOBAL ECONOMY?

OH YES...

I.T.'S BEEN THROUGH ITS OLD RECORDS AND FOUND THAT DAWSON ONCE LOOKED AT A PORN WEBSITE BACK IN 2005...

SO HE'S TECHNICALLY IN BREACH OF HIS CONTRACT... MEANING WE DON'T HAVE TO HONOUR HIS GUARANTEED BONUS... EXCELLENT...

Alex PEATTIE + TAYLOR

I'VE NEVER KNOWN THE FINANCIAL WORLD AS BAD AS THIS, CLIVE. PEOPLE ARE BEING MADE REDUNDANT IN RECORD NUMBERS...

AND, WHILE IN THE PAST WE KNEW WE COULD WALK INTO ANOTHER JOB, WE'RE NOW FACING UP TO NEVER WORKING IN THE CITY AGAIN. IT'S CAUSED A DISCERNABLE CHANGE IN BANKERS' DEMEANOUR...

I'M TALKING ABOUT THE CONTRAST BETWEEN BRASH, ARROGANT AGGRESSIVE BEHAVIOUR AND A HUMBLER, MORE MODEST AND RESTRAINED ATTITUDE...

YES...

WELL, IT'S NICE TO BE FREE TO TELL YOUR BOSS WHAT YOU REALLY THINK OF HIM WHEN YOU'RE FIRED...

INSTEAD OF HAVING TO BITE IT BACK IN CASE YOU BUMP INTO HIM AGAIN IN SOME NEW JOB...

Alex PEATTIE + TAYLOR

SO THE BANK HAS DECIDED TO RENAME BONUSES "RETENTION PAYMENTS"

THAT'S RIGHT...

FOLLOWING THE HUGE SUBPRIME WRITE-DOWNS ANNOUNCED BY BANKS, THERE'S PUBLIC ANGER AT THE IDEA OF US REWARDING STAFF AT A TIME WHEN WE SHOULD BE FOCUSING ON CUTTING COSTS...

BUT THE PRIME FUNCTION OF THE BONUS IS TO ENABLE THE BANK TO HANG ON TO VALUABLE, TALENTED EMPLOYEES. THIS NAME CHANGE WILL HELP REMIND CERTAIN PEOPLE OF THAT FACT...

SO, STILL FRETTING ABOUT YOUR "RETENTION PAYMENT" BEING ZERO, CLIVE? WELL, IT'S CLEARLY AN INDICATION THAT I SHOULD HELP HEADCOUNT REDUCTION BY TENDERING MY RESIGNATION...

46

Strip 1:

IT'S UNTHINKABLE THAT OUR BANK WOULD CYNICALLY PAY OUT LARGE BONUSES THIS YEAR...

DON'T KID YOURSELF, CLIVE...

BUT JUST IMAGINE THE HUGE PUBLIC OUTCRY THAT WOULD RESULT IF, IN THE WAKE OF ALL THE WRITE-DOWNS, BANKERS WERE SEEN TO BE BEING REWARDED FOR FAILURE...

LIKE WE'D CARE?

I'M SORRY, ALEX...BUT I LIKE TO BELIEVE THAT MY EMPLOYER HAS SOME SENSE OF DECENCY AND SENSITIVITY TO PUBLIC OPINION...IT CERTAINLY HELPS ME FEEL BETTER ABOUT MYSELF...

BECAUSE I CAN THINK THAT MY ZERO BONUS WAS JUST THE _NORM_ AND NOT A BLATANT HINT THAT I SHOULD RESIGN.

DREAM ON, CLIVE...

Strip 2:

THERE'S A LOT OF PUBLIC ANGER ABOUT THE PAYMENT OF BONUSES IN BANKS LIKE YOURS THAT ARE EFFECTIVELY NATIONALISED, JEREMY.

YES, ALEX, BUT THE OFFICIAL LINE IS THAT THESE PAYMENTS ARE NECESSARY TO INCENTIVISE AND RETAIN THE TOP TALENT IN THE BANK...

AFTER ALL, WE NEED WORLD-CLASS BANKERS LIKE ME IN PLACE TO RESCUE THE BUSINESS SO IT CAN BE SOLD ONE DAY AND MAKE A PROFIT FOR THE TAX-PAYER...

IT'S A GOOD ARGUMENT...

ER... YES...

AND IT MEANS I OUGHT TO BE HAPPY TO RECEIVE MY BONUS IN BANK SHARES, WHICH WILL BE VALUABLE AGAIN ONCE WE TURN THINGS AROUND.

SO THE FACT THAT YOU WANT YOURS PAID IN _CASH_ IS AN ADMISSION THAT YOU'RE NOT UP TO THE JOB?

IT'S VERY TRICKY...

Strip 3:

I'M TAKING A CERTAIN SADISTIC PLEASURE IN HAVING BEEN SECONDED TO THE GOVERNMENT'S NEW TOXIC BANK.

ZZZ

IT'S FUNNY: I'M SUDDENLY VERY POPULAR BECAUSE I HAVE THE POWER TO BUY UP BANKS' SUB-PRIME DEBT...

SHH, CLIVE. DON'T SAY THAT QUITE SO LOUDLY PLEASE...

IF PEOPLE REALISED WHO YOU WERE, MY BEING WITH YOU MIGHT IMPLY MY BANK HAD FURTHER UNDISCLOSED DODGY ASSETS AND TRIGGER A RUN ON OUR SHARES...

RUMBLE

SPLOT   SPLOT   SPLOT

TOXIC BANK

ARE YOU SURE YOU DON'T WANT TO SHARE MY UMBRELLA?

DON'T BE STUPID... AND DON'T WALK SO CLOSE TO ME...

Strip 4:

I MUST ADMIT I THOUGHT ALL THIS ECOLOGICAL AWARENESS STUFF WAS JUST A BULL MARKET FAD...

POST-CREDIT CRUNCH, I DIDN'T EXPECT PROFESSIONAL CLASS PEOPLE LIKE YOURSELVES TO BOTHER WITH IT ANY MORE...

ON THE CONTRARY, ALEX. IT'S A VERY PRACTICAL LIFESTYLE FOR THE CURRENT ECONOMIC CLIMATE...

WE'RE VERY SELF-SUFFICIENT. WE HAVE A WIND-TURBINE IN OUR GARDEN, WE SOURCE OUR OWN FIREWOOD FROM THE WOODS, WE GROW ORGANIC VEGETABLES AND EVEN KEEP CHICKENS...

EXACTLY...

SO ONCE WE'VE GOT THE 12 FOOT SECURITY FENCE UP, HOPEFULLY WE'LL BE SAFE FROM THE RAMPAGING MOBS...

AFTER ALL, WHEN CIVIL UNREST AND ANARCHY BREAK OUT, IT'S BANKERS LIKE US THEY'RE GOING TO BE LOOKING FOR...

Alex PEATTIE + TAYLOR

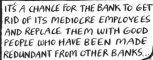

Panel 1: THERE'S A LOT OF TALK ABOUT UPGRADING OF WORKFORCES AT THE MOMENT, CYRUS...

Panel 2: IT'S A CHANCE FOR THE BANK TO GET RID OF ITS MEDIOCRE EMPLOYEES AND REPLACE THEM WITH GOOD PEOPLE WHO HAVE BEEN MADE REDUNDANT FROM OTHER BANKS...

Panel 3: LET ME REMIND YOU THAT, DUE TO THE CREDIT CRUNCH THERE ARE A LOT OF EXTREMELY BRIGHT, HIGHLY EXPERIENCED AND EXCEPTIONALLY WELL-QUALIFIED PEOPLE OUT THERE ON THE JOB MARKET RIGHT NOW...

Panel 4: SO YOU RECKON OUR POSITIONS HERE ARE NOW SAFE?

OH YES... NO BOSS IS EVER GOING TO RISK HIRING ANYONE WHO MIGHT ONE DAY TAKE HIS JOB...

Panel 1: THE CREDIT CRUNCH HAS HAD A DEVASTATING EFFECT ON THE LIVES OF US MIDDLE-CLASS PROFESSIONALS...

Panel 2: DESPITE THE BANK OF ENGLAND'S ATTEMPTS TO STIMULATE THE ECONOMY BY SLASHING INTEREST RATES, THERE SEEMS LITTLE HOPE OF A RETURN TO THE CONSUMER BOOM THAT PEOPLE LIKE US THRIVED IN...

Panel 3: COMPETITIVENESS IS A NATURAL DRIVING FORCE IN OUR WORLD AND WE'RE USED TO ASSERTING OUR SOCIAL STATUS VIA WEALTH AND MATERIAL POSSESSIONS...

≷SIGH≷ YES...

Panel 4: THE TRACKER MORTGAGE ON OUR SIX-BEDROOM HOUSE IN WILTSHIRE IS NOW ONLY £60 A WEEK...

WELL, WE HAVE SEVEN BEDROOMS AND OURS IS ONLY £50... I REMEMBER WHEN PEOPLE USED TO BOAST ABOUT HOW MUCH THEIR HOUSES WERE WORTH...

Panel 1: YOUR STORY SEEMS FAIRLY TYPICAL OF WHAT'S HAPPENING TO BANKERS LIKE YOU WHO LOSE THEIR JOBS AT THE MOMENT, TREVOR.

Panel 2: YOU GET FIRED FROM MEGABANK AND THEN YOU CROP UP A FEW MONTHS LATER AT SOME OBSCURE BANK NO-ONE'S EVER HEARD OF... WHAT'S THAT PLACE YOU'RE NOW WORKING AT CALLED AGAIN?

SECOND NATIONAL BANK OF SASKATCHEWAN...

Panel 3: WHAT A GULF THERE NOW IS BETWEEN US; ONE OF US EMPLOYED BY A GENUINE GLOBAL PLAYER IN THE MARKETS, WHILE THE OTHER WORKS FOR A PIFFLING THIRD-RATE OPERATION....

VERY TRUE...

Panel 4: DUE TO US BEING TOO BACKWARD TO EVER GET INTO SUB-PRIME, MY BANK IS NOW THE FOURTH LARGEST IN THE WORLD BY MARKET CAPITALISATION...

... AND FOLLOWING OUR RECENT SHARE PRICE TRASHING, MEGABANK CURRENTLY RANKS 83RD.

Panel 1: WE BANKERS ARE BEING ACCUSED OF MAKING A FORTUNE FROM ENCOURAGING CONSUMERS TO SPEND INSTEAD OF SAVING...

Panel 2: BUT WE'RE SUFFERING TOO FROM THE RESULTING RECESSION. WE'RE HAVING TO WORK LONGER HOURS FOR LESS MONEY, UNDER MORE PRESSURE, AND WITH NO PROSPECT OF ANY UPTURN FOR MAYBE YEARS TO COME...

Panel 3: GOOD POINT, CLIVE, AND AS ONE SEES ONE'S COLLEAGUES GRIT THEIR TEETH AND GET DOWN TO IT, ONE REALISES THERE'S ONE VICE WE CITY BANKERS CAN'T BE ACCUSED OF...

LAZINESS? SHIRKING A CHALLENGE?

Panel 4: ER, NO: HYPOCRISY. CLEARLY NONE OF US SAVED ANY OF OUR MONEY EITHER...

≷SIGH≷ YES. OTHERWISE WE'D BE ABLE TO AFFORD TO JUST RETIRE AND GET OUT...

LOOK, TRISTRAM, YOU KNOW THAT I RECENTLY LOST MY JOB IN THE CITY...

YES, DAD...

WELL, I'M AFRAID THE BAD NEWS IS THAT I CAN NO LONGER AFFORD TO PAY THE FEES AT THAT PRIVATE BOARDING SCHOOL IN THE COUNTRY THAT WE'VE BEEN SENDING YOU AWAY TO...

SO I'M AFRAID THERE'LL HAVE TO BE A FEW CHANGES. BUT THE GOOD NEWS IS THAT IT MEANS THAT YOU AND I WILL GET TO SEE A LOT MORE OF EACH OTHER...

REALLY?

SO YOUR DAD IS OUR NEW MATHS TEACHER, TRISTRAM?

YES... IT GETS HIM A 50% DISCOUNT ON MY FEES... I BEGGED HIM TO SEND ME TO A STATE SCHOOL INSTEAD...

THIS IS GOING TO BE SO EMBARRASSING...

SO SINCE YOU LOST YOUR JOB AS A BANKER, YOU'RE RETRAINING AS A TEACHER, SIMON?

WELL, WHY NOT?

THE HIGH-FLYING WORLD OF INTERNATIONAL FINANCE IS ALL VERY WELL, BUT IT'S AN ARTIFICIAL AND ISOLATING ENVIRONMENT. IT PUTS US OUT OF TOUCH WITH OTHER ELEMENTS IN SOCIETY...

THAT'S TRUE I SUPPOSE...

BECOMING A SCHOOL TEACHER WILL GIVE ME A CHANCE TO RELATE TO THE YOUNGER GENERATION AND UNDERSTAND THEIR VALUES AND LIFESTYLES.

YES, I CAN SEE YOUR POINT...

I'VE OFTEN WONDERED HOW OUR GRADUATE TRAINEES MANAGE TO SCRAPE BY ON THE £35,000 A YEAR WE PAY THEM, AND ON YOUR NEW SALARY YOU'RE ABOUT TO FIND OUT...

SO YOU'VE DECIDED TO BECOME A TEACHER, SIMON?

YES, THE CITY'S FINISHED POST CREDIT CRUNCH ALEX. WE BOTH KNOW THAT...

THE NEW REGULATORY CODES BEING BROUGHT IN WILL MAKE OUR INDUSTRY UNRECOGNISABLE. SO I THOUGHT IT WAS TIME TO DO SOMETHING WORTHWHILE WITH MY LIFE; TO REPAY MY DEBT TO SOCIETY AS IT WERE...

THERE'S A NEW ETHOS AROUND IN OUR WORLD, ALEX, AND IT'S ALL ABOUT GIVING SOMETHING BACK...

YES...

OUR BONUSES... PEOPLE ARE NOW SUGGESTING THAT THEY SHOULD BE RECOUPABLE BY THE BANK IF OUR DEALS SUBSEQUENTLY GO WRONG...

NOT TO MENTION OUR PENSION POTS... IT'S HORRIFIC... I'M JUST GLAD I'M GETTING OUT...

THIS RECESSION HAS LEFT ALL OF US JUST SITTING AT OUR DESKS, STARING IMPOTENTLY AT OUR SCREENS.

AND WITH OUR BOSSES PROWLING AROUND LOOKING FOR PEOPLE TO FIRE, ANY EVIDENCE OF UNDER-EMPLOYMENT CAN BE FATAL, BUT THERE'S NOTHING TO DO...

HOW ONE YEARNS FOR THE BULL MARKET WHEN ONE WAS PROPERLY BUSY; WHEN ONE'S WORKING DAY WAS FILLED WITH USEFUL, FUNCTIONAL, PURPOSEFUL ACTIVITIES...

FUNNY HEARING A GRADUATE TRAINEE GETTING NOSTALGIC ABOUT BEING SENT OUT TO FETCH OUR COFFEE AND SANDWICHES...

SIGH YES. BACK IN THE DAYS BEFORE WE WERE REDUCED TO DRINKING INSTANT BLEND AND BRINGING IN PACKED LUNCHES.

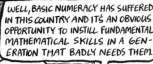

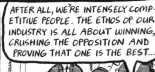

Alex PEATTIE + TAYLOR

DESPITE THE DOWNTURN IT LOOKS LIKE THIS CHARITY CITY QUIZ IS SOLD OUT... HARDLY SURPRISING, CLIVE...

CITY QUIZ

AFTER ALL, WE'RE INTENSELY COMPETITIVE PEOPLE. THE ETHOS OF OUR INDUSTRY IS ALL ABOUT WINNING, CRUSHING THE OPPOSITION AND PROVING THAT ONE IS THE BEST...

FRANKLY IT'S AN INSTINCT THAT'S BEEN FORCIBLY SUPPRESSED BY MARKET EVENTS OF THE LAST EIGHTEEN MONTHS OR SO... THAT'S TRUE...

I MEAN, ABSOLUTELY EVERYONE SCREWED UP ON SUB-PRIME, THUS PROVING THAT WE'RE ALL EQUALLY IGNORANT ON FINANCE... QUITE.. SO LET'S SEE IF WE CAN DO ANY BETTER ON 80's POP MUSIC...

Alex PEATTIE + TAYLOR

I SUPPOSE I'VE ALWAYS SUFFERED FROM "IMPOSTER SYNDROME" THROUGHOUT MY CAREER...

YOU KNOW, THAT SECRET FEELING THAT ONE IS NOT ACTUALLY UP TO ONE'S JOB BUT THAT NO ONE ELSE HAS NOTICED YET... WELL, AS A BANKER THE TRUTH OF IT HAS BECOME OBVIOUS IN RECENT MARKETS...

CAN THERE BE ANYTHING SCARIER THAN WHEN WORLD EVENTS MAKE YOU REALISE THAT YOUR IMPOSTER SYNDROME WAS FULLY JUSTIFIED? ER...YES...

WHEN YOU REALISE THAT IT WAS TRUE ABOUT ABSOLUTELY EVERYONE ELSE TOO — INCLUDING CEOS AND WORLD LEADERS... NOW THAT'S WORRYING... HMM...

alex@alexcartoon.com

Alex PEATTIE + TAYLOR

LOOK AT YOUR PARENTS WORKING AWAY IN THEIR GARDEN ON THEIR 50TH WEDDING ANNIVERSARY... IT'S WHAT THEY LIKE DOING, PENNY...

BUT HOW CAN THEY ENJOY THEIR BIG DAY WHEN THEIR COMFORTABLE RETIREMENT HAS BEEN BLIGHTED BY THE RECESSION WITH ZERO INTEREST RATES WIPING OUT THE INCOME ON THEIR SAVINGS?

THEY'RE PRAGMATIC PEOPLE, PENNY, AND THEY REALISE THAT IN AUSTERE TIMES ONE HAS TO PUT ASIDE SOME OF THE COSY SENTIMENTALITY ASSOCIATED WITH A GOLDEN WEDDING ANNIVERSARY...

WELL, I STILL THINK YOU COULD HAVE CHOSEN A SLIGHTLY MORE PERSONAL GIFT FOR THEM... SO: HOW DEEP SHOULD WE BURY THESE KRUGERRANDS THAT ALEX GAVE US? 5 FEET. TO BE SAFE?

alex@alexcartoon.com

Alex PEATTIE + TAYLOR

ANARCHISTS AND ENVIRONMENTAL PROTESTORS WILL BE TARGETING BANKERS IN THEIR PROTESTS AT THE G20 SUMMIT THIS WEEK...

NEWS

POLICE ARE ADVISING US NOT TO WEAR SUITS, TO CANCEL ALL NON-ESSENTIAL MEETINGS AND PREFERABLY TO STAY AT HOME... WELL, I FOR ONE REFUSE TO BE COWED, CLIVE.

I SHALL BE GOING ABOUT BUSINESS AS NORMAL. AT A TIME WHERE OUR INDUSTRY IS IMPERILLED, THIS IS A PRIME OPPORTUNITY FOR US, BY OUR ACTIONS, TO SEND OUT A CLEAR MESSAGE... TO THE PROTESTORS?

ER, NO: TO OUR COMPETITORS... I MEAN WE WOULDN'T WANT TO ADMIT THAT ALL OUR MEETINGS ARE NON-ESSENTIAL RIGHT NOW, AS WE DON'T HAVE A SNIFF OF ANY BUSINESS...

alex@alexcartoon.com

Alex — PEATTIE + TAYLOR

TO BE HONEST, ALEX, BECOMING A SCHOOL TEACHER MIGHT NOT NECESSARILY BE A LONG-TERM CAREER OPTION FOR ME

WHO KNOWS? PERHAPS IF THE CITY PICKS UP AGAIN IN FOUR OR FIVE YEARS' TIME I MIGHT BE TEMPTED BACK INTO THAT WORLD...

BUT THE IMPORTANT THING IS THAT IN THE MEANTIME I'VE GOT THE OPPORTUNITY TO DO SOMETHING GENUINELY WORTHWHILE AND OF REAL VALUE TO ME ON A PERSONAL LEVEL...

WHAT, GET DIVORCED?

EXACTLY. I MIGHT AS WELL HAVE MY WIFE'S SETTLEMENT WORKED OUT WHILE I'VE STILL GOT NO MONEY...

Alex — PEATTIE + TAYLOR

I SEE YOU HAVE A CLIENT MEETING IN THE CITY AT 11-00,

ALEX... THAT'S RIGHT... I MUST BE GOING SOON...

BUT IN VIEW OF TODAY'S PLANNED ANTI-BANKER DEMONSTRATIONS BY G20 PROTESTORS THE POLICE HAVE ADVISED US TO CANCEL ALL NON-ESSENTIAL MEETINGS

WHAT NONSENSE!

DO YOU REALLY THINK I'M GOING TO ALLOW MY NORMAL WORKING DAY TO BE DISRUPTED BY A BUNCH OF LEFTIES AND TREE-HUGGERS? THIS IS A TIME FOR US TO MAKE A STAND FOR THE VALUES WE BELIEVE IN...

THE LATE MORNING "CLIENT MEETING" HAS ALWAYS BEEN A STANDARD PLOY FOR US TO SLIP OFF FOR AN EARLY LUNCH...

QUITE. I SUGGEST WE BARRICADE OURSELVES IN HERE FOR THE AFTERNOON...

Alex — PEATTIE + TAYLOR

WE BANKERS ARE NOW PUBLIC ENEMY NUMBER ONE - REVILED AS SYMBOLS OF HUBRIS AND GREED...

THE REACTION TO THESE G20 PROTESTS HAS REALLY BROUGHT HOME HOW FAR WE'VE COME FROM OUR HEYDAY WHEN WE WERE ROLE MODELS FOR WEALTH AND SUCCESS...

NOW SUDDENLY WE'RE EXPECTED TO HANG OUR HEADS IN SHAME, TO KEEP A LOW PROFILE AND MAKE EVERY EFFORT NOT TO LOOK LIKE BANKERS. HOW'S THAT SUPPOSED TO MAKE US FEEL?

REALLY NOSTALGIC... SIGH... EVERYONE IS IN DRESS DOWN... IT'S JUST LIKE THE DOTCOM BOOM OR THE HEDGE FUND BONANZA...

BUT WE'LL ALL BE BACK IN OUR CONFORMIST SUITS TOMORROW AS WE SUCK UP TO OUR BOSSES AND TRY TO KEEP OUR JOBS...

Alex — PEATTIE + TAYLOR

THE THREAT OF REDUNDANCY IS LOOMING LARGE OVER ALL US CITY BANKERS RIGHT NOW...

BUT ITS SERIOUSNESS DEPENDS ON WHAT GENERATION YOU'RE FROM... YOU'RE STILL RELATIVELY YOUNG, ALAN... IF YOU WERE TO LOSE YOUR JOB THE EXPECTATION IS THAT YOU'LL FIND WORK AGAIN EVENTUALLY,

BUT LOOK AT ME... I'M PUSHING FIFTY AND NEARING THE END OF MY CAREER... IF I WERE TO GET THE PUSH AT MY TIME OF LIFE IT'D BE A VERY DIFFERENT PROSPECT.

I COULD JUST CLAIM THAT I'D "RETIRED" WHEREAS YOU'D BE TARRED WITH THE STIGMA OF "UNEMPLOYED"...

NO NEED TO RUB IT IN, ALEX...

Alex PEATTIE + TAYLOR

FRANKLY LAST WEEK'S G20 DEMONSTRATIONS AGAINST GLOBAL CAPITALISM BY ANARCHISTS AND GREENS WERE A JOKE...

THE BEST THE PROTESTORS COULD DO TO TAUNT US WAS DRESS UP IN WHAT THEY THINK BANKERS WEAR: CHALK-STRIPE SUIT, BOWLER HAT AND OLD-FASHIONED ROLLED, BLACK UMBRELLA.

SOME IMAGE OF A CITY GENT DRAWN FROM THE 1950's... PAH! HOW SATIRICAL OR RELEVANT TO THE MODERN DAY IS _THAT_ SUPPOSED TO BE...?

ER, VERY... THAT'S THE ERA OF BANKING WE'LL BE GOING BACK TO... OH GOD... NO RISK-TAKING, NO BONUSES, MODEST PAY, DULL 9-5 RESPECTABILITY...

IT'S AN APPALLING PROSPECT, CLIVE...

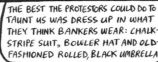

Alex PEATTIE + TAYLOR

THE FINANCIAL WORLD HAS HAD TO COME TO TERMS WITH THE PUBLIC ANGER OVER EXECUTIVE BONUSES...

BONUSES WERE SUPPOSED TO BE EX GRATIA PAYMENTS AWARDED TO INDIVIDUALS WHO HAVE PERFORMED WELL IN A GIVEN YEAR, YET BANKERS HAVE COME TO VIEW THEM AS AN ENTITLEMENT...

CLEARLY SUCH PAY-OUTS ARE UNACCEPTABLE AT A TIME WHERE BANKS HAVE LOST MONEY AND ACCEPTED TAXPAYER FUNDING; A RADICAL OVERHAUL OF HOW BANKERS ARE REMUNERATED WAS REQUIRED.

YES..

SO WE JUST DOUBLED EVERYONE'S SALARIES...

IT SEEMS AN ELEGANT SOLUTION - AFTER ALL, WE COULDN'T BE EXPECTED TO GO WITHOUT...

Alex PEATTIE + TAYLOR

WHAT'S THIS, CLIVE? FLOWERS FOR ME? YOU MUST BE FEELING GUILTY ABOUT SOMETHING...

DON'T BE SILLY, BRIDGET. I JUST GOT THEM FOR YOU AS A SPONTANEOUS GIFT... I THOUGHT YOU'D LIKE THEM.

BUT IT'S NOT MY BIRTHDAY OR VALENTINE'S DAY...

THAT'S EXACTLY MY POINT. FLOWERS ARE SOMETHING A WOMAN SHOULD BE ABLE TO ENJOY ANY DAY OF THE YEAR AND NOT JUST CONFINED TO A FEW SPECIFIC FORMAL OCCASIONS LAID DOWN BY SOCIETY...

SO HOW DID SHE REACT WHEN YOU GOT ROUND TO MENTIONING THAT DUE TO BUDGETARY CUTBACKS YOU WEREN'T ABLE TO GET HER CORPORATE INVITE TO THE CHELSEA FLOWER SHOW THIS YEAR?

BADLY.

Alex PEATTIE + TAYLOR

HELLO, CYRUS, I JUST THOUGHT I'D LET YOU KNOW THAT I'VE RETURNED FROM MY SECONDMENT AT THE TOXIC BANK...

THAT'S GOOD TO KNOW, CLIVE. I CAN TELL YOU THE BUSINESS DOWNTURN HAS HIT MEGABANK PRETTY BAD SINCE YOU'VE BEEN AWAY. WE NEEDED PEOPLE OF YOUR CALIBER ON THE TEAM.

SO ALL I CAN SAY IS IT'S GREAT TO HAVE YOU BACK...

DID YOU MISS ME?

WE SURE DID!

...IN THE LAST ROUND OF REDUNDANCIES... WE TOTALLY FORGOT YOU EXISTED... BUT NOW THAT YOU'RE HERE...

AAARGH! CLIVE?

Strip 1

WELL IT'S BEEN A PLEASURE TO SEE YOU, ALEX, AND IT'S ALWAYS GOOD FOR A FINANCIAL JOURNALIST LIKE ME TO TALK TO BANKERS...

BUT WHEN YOU PHONED ME UP AND SUGGESTED WE MET FOR LUNCH YOU IMPLIED THAT YOU MIGHT HAVE SOME SORT OF STORY FOR ME...

WELL, NOT AS SUCH...

BUT AS YOU WORK FOR A WELL-RESPECTED NEWSWIRE SERVICE I THOUGHT IT'D BE USEFUL FOR YOU TO GET SOME GENERAL BACKGROUND ON HOW THE BANKING SECTOR IS COPING IN THE RECESSION...

BADLY, I IMAGINE...

YOU'RE RIGHT...

OUR EXPENSES HAVE BEEN SLASHED, WHICH IS WHY I CALLED YOU, AS, TO MAINTAIN IMPARTIALITY, YOU JOURNOS AREN'T ALLOWED TO ACCEPT LUNCHES FROM ANYONE...

YOUR BILL, SIR...

THANKS. I'LL HAVE ANOTHER BRANDY BEFORE YOU GO...

Strip 2

THE MARKET HAS RALLIED, WITH BANK STOCKS LEADING THE WAY... MAYBE WE'RE OUT OF THE WOODS...

MMM...

I'M STILL BEARISH, CLIVE... I DON'T THINK THE BANKS HAVE SUCCEEDED YET IN POSITIONING THEMSELVES FOR RECOVERY OR IN RESTORING PUBLIC CONFIDENCE...

YOU CAN GAUGE THE SUCCESS OF ANY BUSINESS BY ASKING THIS QUESTION: ARE THEY GAINING OR LOSING CUSTOMERS?

AND I'M AFRAID THE BANKING SECTOR HAS BEEN GOING THE WRONG WAY ON THAT ONE...

INDEED...

...THEY'RE GAINING CUSTOMERS, AS PEOPLE FRANTICALLY OPEN NEW ACCOUNTS TO SPREAD THEIR MONEY AROUND... QUITE. EVERYONE'S STILL PARANOID THE BANKS MIGHT GO BUST...

Strip 3

I'VE GOT 2 TICKETS TO THE CHELSEA GAME TONIGHT. I THOUGHT WITH YOUR PERMISSION I'D TAKE A CLIENT, ALEX...

I'M NOT SURE THAT'S APPROPRIATE...

"FLASHING ONE'S CASH" IS DEEMED OUT OF KEEPING WITH THE CURRENT MOOD OF AUSTERITY. SO THE BANK HAS BANNED ALL CORPORATE HOSPITALITY...OF COURSE IT'S JUST COVERT COST-CUTTING...

THAT'S ABSURD.

IN THE PRESENT TOUGH AND UNCERTAIN BUSINESS CLIMATE SURELY THERE'S AN ADVANTAGE TO BE GAINED BY USING SPORTING FIXTURES TO ENTERTAIN THE RIGHT PEOPLE?

ABSOLUTELY.

STARTING WITH ME... I ASSUME YOU WANT TO SUCK UP TO ME TO KEEP YOUR JOB? AND HOW ELSE AM I GOING TO GET TO SEE ANY MATCHES THESE DAYS?

GRAB

Strip 4

JUST A COUPLE OF YEARS AGO BANKERS WERE RESPECTED PROFESSIONALS... THEN CAME THE CREDIT CRUNCH...

PROPERTY PRICES COLLAPSED, EQUITY MARKETS WERE TRASHED, COMMODITY VALUES ANNIHILATED... AND IT'S ALL BEEN BLAMED ON THE SHORT-TERMISM AND EXCESSES OF PEOPLE LIKE US...

YES INDEED...

IT'S CERTAINLY FORCED US TO RE-EVALUATE OUR OSTENTATIOUS MATERIALISTIC LIFESTYLES AND THE SHALLOW, FRIVOLOUS STATUS SYMBOLS WE SPENT OUR MONEY ON...

THAT'S TRUE...

LIKE OUR PORSCHES... THEY NOW LOOK LIKE QUITE SENSIBLE INVESTMENTS COMPARED WITH OUR OTHER ASSETS...

WELL ONE EXPECTS SPORTS CARS TO MASSIVELY DEPRECIATE IN VALUE...

BLIP

BLIP

FLASH!

FLASH!

BANK CAR PARK

 **WELL, THE GOOD THING ABOUT THE ECONOMIC DOWNTURN IS NONE OF MY GUYS WILL BE EXPECTING BONUSES THIS YEAR...**

 **AND THEY'RE ALL SO TOTALLY FEARFUL AND DEMORALIZED THAT THEY'LL COUNT THEMSELVES LUCKY JUST TO HAVE JOBS AND WON'T BE LOOKING FOR NEW ONES...**

GOOD POINT, CYRUS

 **BUT AT THE SAME TIME THEY'RE STILL GOING TO BE GETTING REGULAR CALLS FROM HEADHUNTERS... DON'T FORGET WHAT THAT CAN DO FOR A BANKER'S EGO...**

TRUE.

 **=SIGH= HEADHUNTERS THESE DAYS ARE NEVER TRYING TO RECRUIT YOU; JUST OFFER YOU THE CANDIDATES THEY'VE GOT ON THEIR BOOKS...**

WHICH REMINDS US HOW MANY PEOPLE OUT THERE COULD DO OUR JOBS... AND CHEAPER. IT'S DEPRESSING...

 **RECENT DATA SEEMS TO SUGGEST THAT THE PROPERTY MARKET MAY BE RECOVERING...**

WELL, WE'VE JUST BOUGHT A HOUSE...

 **THE TIMING WAS RIGHT FOR US TO MOVE AND WITH THE LOW INTEREST RATES BROUGHT IN TO STIMULATE THE ECONOMY, IT WAS QUITE AFFORDABLE.**

INTERESTING...

 **THIS IS EVIDENCE OF HOW SERIOUSLY THIS RECESSION IS ACTUALLY AFFECTING THOSE CRUCIAL PROFESSIONAL CLASS PEOPLE LIKE YOURSELVES...**

YES...

 **WE'VE HAD TO PULL OUR THREE BOYS OUT OF ETON...**

AND SO WE NEEDED TO GET OURSELVES INTO THE CATCHMENT AREA FOR A DECENT STATE SCHOOL...

IT'S ALL UTTERLY SCARY...

 **ONE OF THE BIGGEST ADVANTAGES OF MY NEW JOB AS A TEACHER IS THE SIXTEEN WEEKS ANNUAL HOLIDAY...**

 **CONTRAST THAT WITH WHEN I WAS A BANKER AND HAD TO WORK ALL THE HOURS GOD SENT, INCLUDING MOST WEEKENDS AND QUITE A FEW FAMILY HOLIDAYS...**

 **ALL THIS FREE TIME I'VE GOT NOW HAS REALLY HELPED EASE THE TENSION IN MY RELATIONSHIP WITH MY WIFE...**

I'M GLAD TO HEAR IT...

 **YES, SHE USED TO THINK SHE HATED MY JOB BUT SHE'S NOW REALISED IT'S ACTUALLY ME THAT SHE HATES...**

SO SHE'S HAPPY TO GO ALONG WITH YOUR PLAN TO GET DIVORCED?

 **SO YOU'RE PLANNING A BUSINESS TRIP TO THE VATICAN NEXT MONTH, ALEX?**

WELL, WHY NOT?

 **THE CHURCH OF ROME HAS MONEY, CLIVE; PLENTY OF IT, AND SO MUST NEED PROFESSIONAL ADVICE ON ITS INVESTMENT STRATEGY.**

IT DOESN'T SEEM RIGHT SOMEHOW

 **ONE THINKS OF HIS HOLINESS THE POPE AS A SPIRITUAL FIGURE WHOM ONE IMAGINES AS BEING ALOOF AND UNCONCERNED WITH THE MUNDANE REALITIES OF THE EVERYDAY WORLD...**

 **WHAT, LIKE FOOTBALL? YES, LET'S HOPE SO...**

WELL, YOU WOULDN'T WANT HIM TO REALISE THAT YOUR TRIP TO ROME WAS JUST A PRETEXT TO GET YOURSELF TO THE CHAMPIONS LEAGUE FINAL ON EXPENSES.

Strip 1

 A LOT OF BANKS HAVE REPORTED BETTER THAN EXPECTED PROFITS THIS WEEK...

 OF COURSE THE GOVERNMENT WANTS OUR SECTOR TO RESUME LENDING IN ORDER TO STIMULATE CONSUMER SPENDING... BUT WILL IT WORK?

HMM...

 WELL I THINK FOR MANY PEOPLE THE SENSIBLE PRIORITY RIGHT NOW IS TO USE ANY SURPLUS CASH TO PAY OFF DEBTS...

 SUCH AS THE DEBTS THE BANKS OWE TO THE GOVERNMENT FOR THE BAIL-OUT?

QUITE. AND ONCE WE'RE NO LONGER BEHOLDEN THERE WE CAN GO BACK TO AWARDING OURSELVES OUR CUSTOMARY BONUSES...

HAPPY DAYS...

Strip 2

 WELL THE BANK HAS ADDRESSED TWO OF THE ISSUES WE'RE ACCUSED OF BEING IN THE WRONG ABOUT SINCE THE CREDIT CRUNCH AND THE BAIL-OUT...

 FIRST: WE'RE NOT PAYING ANY EXECUTIVES BONUSES THIS YEAR. INSTEAD WE'RE DEFERRING THEM UNTIL MARKETS RECOVER.

 AND SECOND: THANKS TO THE BANK OF ENGLAND'S LOWER INTEREST RATES POLICY, WE'VE GONE BACK TO OUR CORE BUSINESS OF LENDING MONEY...

INDEED.

 TO OURSELVES...WE'RE ISSUING THE MONEY FOR OUR BONUSES AS ZERO-RATE LOANS, REPAYABLE WHENEVER...

WHENEVER WE'RE ALLOWED TO GET BONUSES AGAIN, YES...

Strip 3

 DID YOUR TWO COMPANIONS LEAVE EARLY, SIR?

:SIGH: YES...

 THEY BOTH HAD TO RUSH BACK TO THEIR OFFICES, I'M AFRAID... _UNLIKE_ MYSELF... IT'S A SAD REFLECTION OF OUR RESPECTIVE DIFFERING FORTUNES AT THE MOMENT...

 WE ALL SUFFER IN A MARKET DOWNTURN... REGRETTABLY IT ALSO BECOMES APPARENT JUST WHOSE BUSINESS HAS BEEN HIT WORSE...

YES SIR...

 THEIRS... FROM THE WAY THEY BOTH SCARPERED WHEN THE BILL CAME... I ASSUME THEIR EXPENSES HAVE BEEN DOWNGRADED...

TO THINK: LAST YEAR WE'D HAVE ALL BEEN FIGHTING OVER WHO GOT TO PAY...

Strip 4

 THE SIMULATOR WHICH YOU'RE SITTING IN IS AN EXACT MOCK-UP OF AN AIRLINE CABIN...

BRITISH A...

 AND IT WILL REPLICATE THE EXPERIENCE OF A PLANE JOURNEY IN EVERY DETAIL AS WE DO TODAY'S FLIGHT SAFETY AWARENESS CORPORATE BONDING EXERCISE...

 LET ME ASSURE YOU: WHAT YOU WILL GAIN FROM DOING THIS COURSE WILL PROVE VALUABLE TO ANYONE WHO FLIES REGULARLY...

OH GOOD...

 SO WE DO GET AIR MILES... MY COLLEAGUE AND I WERE WONDERING...

I CAN'T SEE THE POINT OF WASTING A MORNING HERE IF WE DIDN'T...

Alex PEATTIE + TAYLOR

 FOR THIS FLIGHT SAFETY AWARENESS COURSE YOU ARE IN A MOCK-UP OF A NORMAL AIRCRAFT CABIN...

 NOW, IN DEALING WITH EMERGENCY SITUATIONS THAT MIGHT ARISE IN AIR TRAVEL THE MOST IMPORTANT THING IS FORWARD PLANNING...

 YOU NEED TO ANTICIPATE THE WORST-CASE SCENARIO AND WORK OUT IN ADVANCE HOW YOU'D GET OUT OF HERE... EASY...

 I'D HAVE MYSELF UPGRADED AT CHECK-IN... I MEAN WE ARE IN ECONOMY CLASS, AREN'T WE? WITH ALL THE COST-CUTTING IT COULD HAPPEN TO ANY OF US...

Alex PEATTIE + TAYLOR

 THE NEXT STAGE IN THIS FLIGHT SAFETY AWARENESS COURSE IS A SIMULATED EMERGENCY LANDING...

 THE CABIN WILL FILL WITH SMOKE AND WE WILL BE TOLD TO EVACUATE. WHEN THAT HAPPENS DON'T BARGE OTHERS ASIDE AND PUSH YOUR WAY TO THE FRONT...

 IT'S IMPORTANT TO RETAIN ONE'S DIGNITY AND CREATE THE RIGHT IMPRESSION ON OTHER PASSENGERS... THAT ONE IS BRITISH AND, ABOVE ALL, A GENTLEMAN?

 ER, NO... THAT ONE IS ACCUSTOMED TO TRAVELLING FIRST CLASS WHERE THEY ALWAYS LET YOU OFF THE PLANE FIRST...

Alex PEATTIE + TAYLOR

 THAT AIR FLIGHT EMERGENCY SCENARIO WAS SO REALISTIC... BRITISH AI

 YOU KNEW YOU WERE JUST IN A SIMULATOR IN A HANGAR BUT WHEN THE CABIN BEGAN TO ROCK AND FILL WITH SMOKE YOU INSTINCTIVELY PANICKED...

 IT WAS HARD NOT TO BELIEVE YOU WERE ON AN ACTUAL PLANE... ONLY CYRUS SEEMED ABLE TO STAY CALM AND KEEP A GRIP ON THE REALITY OF THE SITUATION...

 HEY, THIS FLIGHT'S GREAT. YOU CAN HAVE YOUR BLACKBERRY SWITCHED ON THE WHOLE TIME... ER, SIR. YOU WERE SUPPOSED TO EVACUATE FIVE MINUTES AGO...

Alex PEATTIE + TAYLOR

 THAT EMERGENCY PLANE EVACUATION DRILL SHOULD HAVE BEEN CALM AND DIGNIFIED...

 BUT IT TURNED INTO A STAMPEDE... HYSTERIA SET IN AND PEOPLE WERE BARGING OTHER PASSENGERS OUT OF THE WAY AND TRAMPLING THEM UNDERFOOT... IT WAS SCARY, CLIVE...

 AND IT SERVED AS A GRIM REMINDER OF THE ULTIMATE NIGHTMARE AIR FLIGHT SCENARIO WHICH ONE HOPES NEVER TO FACE...

 WHAT, HAVING TO TRAVEL ON A NO-FRILLS AIRLINE WITH UNALLOCATED SEATING? THAT'S WHAT IT'S LIKE WHEN YOU BOARD, I'M TOLD...

Alex PEATTIE + TAYLOR

Strip 1

THE VALUE OF TODAY'S FLIGHT SAFETY EXERCISE? WELL, CORPORATIONS CAN BE IMPERSONAL ENTITIES...

BUT INDIVIDUALS WITHIN THEM NEED TO HAVE A COLLECTIVE SENSE OF IDENTIFICATION WITH WHAT DEFINES THEIR COMPANY...

THIS SIMULATION ALLOWS YOU TO ENGAGE METAPHORICALLY WITH ABSTRACT REALITIES WHICH ARE IMPORTANT. THE KEY PHRASE FOR YOU IS "SHARE EXPERIENCE."

HUH?

WHAT, BEING IN A CRASH AND THEN ALL GOING DOWN IN AN ENORMOUS SLIDE?

YES...

IT'S JUST LIKE WHAT WAS EXPERIENCED BY THE BANK'S SHARES...

OH YES

AND IT'S LIKE WHAT'S GOING TO HAPPEN TO YOU TOO IF WE DON'T GET THE PRICE BACK UP...

ULP

Strip 2

WE'VE HAD TO MAKE A LOT OF DOMESTIC ECONOMIES SINCE I LOST MY JOB IN THE CITY IN JANUARY, ALEX...

WE'VE CANCELLED OUR USUAL FAMILY HOLIDAY IN TUSCANY, WE DON'T EAT OUT ANYMORE, I'VE SOLD MY PORSCHE AND PUT OUR SECOND HOME ON THE MARKET...

BUT ONE AREA OF MY LIFE IS SACROSANCT... I'D NEVER ALLOW COST-CUTTING TO IMPINGE ON ANYTHING CONNECTED TO MY CHILDREN'S EDUCATION...

SO, DARLING, WE COULD ALWAYS GET RID OF THE NANNY AND YOU COULD TAKE THE KIDS TO SCHOOL...?

WHAT, AND HAVE ALL THE MUMS REALISE I'M UNEMPLOYED? NO FEAR...

Strip 3

THE GOVERNMENT'S PLAN TO BEAT THE RECESSION RELIES ON BOOSTING CONSUMER SPENDING...

OF COURSE BANKS ARE BEING BLAMED FOR CAUSING THIS MESS, SO IT'S GOOD TO KNOW WE HAVE A KEY ROLE TO PLAY IN STIMULATING ECONOMIC RECOVERY...

AFTER ALL, WE PROVIDE THE FINANCE THAT PEOPLE CAN THEN GO OUT AND SPEND ON CONSUMER GOODS AND SERVICES, HOLIDAYS ETC...

YES INDEED...

IT'S NICE TO BE ABLE TO PUT A POSITIVE SPIN ON MASS FIRINGS...

WELL, BANKERS BLOWING THEIR REDUNDANCY CHEQUES IS ABOUT THE ONLY THING PROPPING UP THE ECONOMY RIGHT NOW...

Strip 4

I UNDERSTAND YOUR RESTAURANT IS PARTICIPATING IN THIS "TWO MEALS FOR THE PRICE OF ONE" NEWSPAPER OFFER...

THAT'S RIGHT, SIR. BUSINESS IS TOUGH AT THE MOMENT... I'M NOT SURPRISED. THERE ARE CUTBACKS AND RESTRICTIONS GOING ON EVERYWHERE...

SO, A TABLE FOR TWO, SIR? YES, PLEASE... AND HERE'S THE TWO-FOR-ONE COUPON FOR OUR MEALS...

AND HERE'S ANOTHER ONE FOR THE TWO "CLIENTS" WE'RE ENTERTAINING...

WE'LL TAKE THEIR SHARE IN WINE, PLEASE...

59

ALEX WENT TO A HEALTH SPA.

Strip 1

Alex — PEATTIE + TAYLOR

Panel 1: WE BANKERS ARE NOT RENOWNED FOR FORWARD THINKING... BUT SOMETIMES IT'S IMPORTANT TO LOOK AHEAD AND PLAN FOR THE FUTURE...

Panel 2: BRITAIN'S NORTH SEA ENERGY IS DUE TO RUN OUT SOON, SO WE NEED TO START FORGING RELATIONSHIPS WITH COMPANIES IN PLACES LIKE SOUTH AFRICA WHICH HAS LARGE RESERVES OF COAL AND URANIUM... / OH I KNOW WHAT THIS IS ALL ABOUT...

Panel 3: WITH THE BRITISH LIONS RUGBY TOUR OF SOUTH AFRICA COMING UP, YOU'RE LOOKING FOR A PRETEXT TO FLY OUT THERE ON BUSINESS... / REALLY, CLIVE. HOW CAN YOU ACCUSE ME OF JUST THINKING ABOUT SHORT-TERM FREEBIES?

Panel 4: I'M THINKING OF LONG-TERM FREEBIES TOO... DON'T FORGET: NEXT YEAR IT'S THE FOOTBALL WORLD CUP, ALSO IN SOUTH AFRICA... / OF COURSE... SO WE'LL NEED A PRETEXT THAT WILL GET US OUT THERE FOR THAT TOO... / QUITE...

Strip 2

Panel 1: YOU'RE AN INTELLIGENT BOY, CHRISTOPHER, BUT IF YOU WANT TO FOLLOW ME INTO THE CITY YOU'LL NEED GUIDANCE...

Panel 2: BUT, DAD, EVEN IF I WANTED TO WORK IN THE BUSINESS WORLD I'M NOT SURE THAT THE STUFF YOU'RE TELLING ME WILL STILL BE RELEVANT IN A FEW YEARS... / NONSENSE.

Panel 3: IT'S IMPORTANT TO SHOW HOW FAMILIAR YOU ARE WITH THE MODERN FINANCIAL PRODUCTS. NOW, REMEMBERING WHAT I'VE TOLD YOU, CAN YOU EXPLAIN HOW CREDIT DERIVATIVES WORK? / LET'S SEE...

Panel 4: NOT REALLY... ALL THAT TECHNICAL STUFF IS A BIT OVER MY HEAD... / GOOD. IT'S IMPORTANT NOT TO SOUND LIKE ONE OF THE BRAINY QUANTS THAT GOT US INTO THE SUB-PRIME MESS... / THIS AFTERNOON I'LL TEACH YOU HOW TO ORDER OFF A WINE LIST...

Strip 3

Panel 1: SO THE BANK'S "STRUCTURED CREDIT DIVISION" IS NOW TO BE KNOWN AS THE "FINANCIALS DIVISION".

Panel 2: WELL, THEY'RE THE GUYS WHO LOST ALL THE MONEY ON SUB-PRIME. / SO WE RENAME THEIR DEPARTMENT AND IGNORE THE PROBLEM... TYPICAL...

Panel 3: YOU KNOW HOW IT IS, CLIVE. EVERYTHING THESE DAYS IS ABOUT SPIN AND PRESENTATION AND LOOKING GOOD IN PUBLIC...

Panel 4: WELL, I JUST HOPE NONE OF THOSE PEOPLE WILL BE GETTING BONUSES THIS YEAR... / OF COURSE NOT...

Panel 5: THEY'LL BE GETTING "RETENTION PAYMENTS". THE BANK'S NOT STUPID...

Strip 4

Panel 1: I KNOW GLOBAL WARMING IS SUPPOSED TO BE INEVITABLE, BUT I REFUSE TO JOIN THE DOOM-MONGERS...

Panel 2: AFTER ALL, THE LAST TWO SUMMERS IN THIS COUNTRY HAVE BEEN CONSIDERABLY WETTER THAN USUAL AND FOR ALL WE KNOW THIS YEAR MIGHT BE ANOTHER ONE... / YOU'RE IN DENIAL, CLIVE...

Panel 3: METEOROLOGISTS ARE PREDICTING A HOT, DRY SUMMER, WHICH WILL INCREASINGLY BE THE TREND. IN OTHER WORDS IN THE LONGER TERM WE'RE DOOMED...

Panel 4: WHAT, NEVER TO WIN ANOTHER ASHES SERIES? / QUITE. WITHOUT ANY DECENT RAIN TO GET ENGLAND THE ODD DRAW I'M BETTING ON A 5-0 AUSSIE VICTORY.

alex@alexcartoon.com

Row 1 — Alex (Peattie + Taylor)

Panel 1: THAT'S IT...I'M CALLING MY HEADHUNTER RIGHT AWAY... / WHAT HAPPENED?

Panel 2: CYRUS CALLED ME INTO HIS OFFICE TO GIVE ME THE STANDARD PEP TALK: HOW TOUGH THINGS ARE RIGHT NOW WITH THE LACK OF DEALS ETC ETC...

Panel 3: HE STRESSED HOW KEEN HE IS TO RETAIN KEY PEOPLE LIKE ME, BUT THEN OFFERED A PRETTY DAMNING INDICATION OF JUST HOW BLEAK THE FINANCIAL OUTLOOK IS... / REALLY?

Panel 4: YES. HE GAVE ME A PAY RISE... / OH GOD... THAT'S A SURE SIGN THERE WON'T BE ANY BONUSES THIS YEAR...

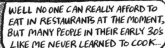

Row 2 — Alex (Peattie + Taylor)

Panel 1: PIZZA COMPANIES ARE APPARENTLY A GOOD INVESTMENT IN THIS RECESSION...

Panel 2: WELL NO ONE CAN REALLY AFFORD TO EAT IN RESTAURANTS AT THE MOMENT, BUT MANY PEOPLE IN THEIR EARLY 30's LIKE ME NEVER LEARNED TO COOK...

Panel 3: IT STANDS TO REASON... BACK IN THE ECONOMIC GOOD TIMES I GREW UP IN THERE WAS NEVER ANY NEED FOR A YOUNG, SUCCESSFUL PERSON TO EAT AT HOME... / NO.

Panel 4: YOU WERE ALWAYS WORKING LATE IN YOUR OFFICE WITH YOUR TEAM AND SENDING OUT FOR TAKEAWAYS... / SIGH / THIS STUFF MAKES ME SO NOSTALGIC FOR THE DAYS WHEN WE ACTUALLY HAD SOME DEALS ON... / CHOMP

Row 3 — Alex (Peattie + Taylor)

Panel 1: REMARKABLY THE STOCK MARKET HAS RECOVERED BY 25% OVER RECENT MONTHS...

Panel 2: BUT THE SAME THING HAPPENED IN 1930, BEFORE MARKETS PLUNGED TO NEW LOWS, WHICH IS WHY MANY FUND MANAGERS LIKE MYSELF HAVE KEPT THEIR FUNDS IN CASH OF LATE.

Panel 3: SO DOES THIS REFLECT REAL UNDERLYING CONFIDENCE? / WELL I'M MAKING NO SECRET OF THE FACT THAT I REMAIN FIRMLY NEGATIVE, BEARISH AND PESSIMISTIC IN MY OUTLOOK... / WELL THAT COULDN'T BE CLEARER...

Panel 4: SO YOU THINK IT'S A GENUINE RECOVERY AND YOU'RE CROSS THAT YOU DIDN'T MAKE ANY MONEY OUT OF IT? / EXACTLY. HENCE MY NEED TO TALK THE MARKET DOWN SO I CAN GET BACK IN AT THE BOTTOM...

Row 4 — Alex (Peattie + Taylor)

Panel 1: GLOBALISATION IS NOW A DIRTY WORD. AFTER ALL IT MERELY CREATED BANKS THAT WERE TOO BIG TO FAIL...

Panel 2: THEIR SIZE AND UNWIELDINESS ALLOWED THEM TO BECOME HUGELY EXPOSED TO SUB PRIME DEBT WHICH MEANT THEY HAD TO BE RESCUED BY THE GOVERNMENT...

Panel 3: THIS HAS OPENED THE MARKET TO BOUTIQUE INVESTMENT HOUSES LIKE MINE. BEING SMALL, LEAN AND NIMBLE WE ARE ABLE TO OFFER SOMETHING THE LARGER BANKS CAN'T... / YES...

Panel 4: JOB PACKAGES WITH GUARANTEED BONUSES... / WELL AS WE HAVEN'T HAD TO BE BAILED OUT BY THE TAXPAYER THERE ARE NO CONSTRAINTS ON US. / ANY CHANCE OF FINDING SOMETHING FOR ME?

Alex PEATTIE + TAYLOR

PENNY, WE'LL BE STAYING WITH ROBIN THORNE AFTER GLYNDEBOURNE THIS WEEKEND. HIS HOUSE IS IN THE AREA...

YOUR EX-GRADUATE TRAINEE? BUT DIDN'T YOU AND HE FALL OUT WHEN HE SET UP A REALLY SUCCESSFUL HEDGE FUND AND BECAME SUPER RICH?

GOODNESS ME, A LOT OF WATER'S GONE UNDER THE BRIDGE SINCE THEN... AS A MATTER OF FACT HIS HEDGE FUND WENT BUST LAST YEAR...

BUT HE'S INVITED YOU TO STAY SO YOU MUST HAVE PATCHED THINGS UP...

NOT EXACTLY...

OH GOD... WHAT ARE *YOU* DOING HERE, ALEX?

I'D HEARD THAT YOU'D BEEN FORCED TO OPEN YOUR HOUSE AS A B+B, ROBIN...

GUEST HOUSE

Alex PEATTIE + TAYLOR

I'M NOT SURE I FEEL ENTIRELY COMFORTABLE STAYING IN THIS B+B RUN BY YOUR EX-GRADUATE TRAINEE, ALEX...

ESPECIALLY AS HE HAD TO OPEN IT BECAUSE HIS HEDGE FUND WENT BUST... ARE YOU SURE YOU'RE NOT JUST DOING THIS TO EMBARRASS HIM?

LOOK, PENNY, I HADN'T SEEN ROBIN IN A WHILE AND I THOUGHT IT WOULD PROVIDE AN OPPORTUNITY FOR US TO CATCH UP ON OLD TIMES...

AH... YOU GETTING MY BREAKFAST, ROBIN... JUST LIKE BACK IN '99... I HOPE YOU HAVEN'T FORGOTTEN HOW I LIKE MY MARMITE...

SEETHE

Alex PEATTIE + TAYLOR

I USED TO RUN A SO-CALLED HEDGE FUND, ALEX, BUT IN REALITY WE WEREN'T HEDGED AT ALL...

WE JUST LEVERAGED UP THE CAPITAL WE RAISED, PUNTED IT ALL ON THE MARKET GOING UP AND PAID OURSELVES 20% OF THE PROFITS FOR OUR "EXPERTISE"...

OF COURSE AS SOON AS THE MARKETS CRASHED WE LOST ALL OF OUR INVESTORS' MONEY. WE WERE QUITE IRRESPONSIBLE REALLY... I SUPPOSE IT WAS ONLY RIGHT AND FAIR THAT WE WENT BUST...

BECAUSE NOW YOU CAN SET UP A NEW HEDGE FUND AND START PAYING YOURSELVES PROFITS RIGHT AWAY?

INSTEAD OF CONTINUING WITH THE OLD ONE AND HAVING TO MAKE BACK THE LOSSES FIRST... YES, THAT'S THE PLAN...

MARKETS BOOM AGAIN

Alex PEATTIE + TAYLOR

TYPICAL! NONE OF YOU PEOPLE EVER READ E-MAILS FROM US IN I.T.

WE TRY NOT TO...

WE LET EVERYONE KNOW LAST WEEK THAT WE WERE UPGRADING THE BANK'S SECURITY SYSTEM TODAY... OBVIOUSLY THERE WERE BOUND TO BE SOME TECHNICAL GLITCHES...

BUT THESE DAYS EVERYONE TAKES COMPUTER-BASED SYSTEMS FOR GRANTED, EXPECTS THEM TO FUNCTION PERFECTLY AND HAS NO PATIENCE WITH THEM WHEN THEY DON'T...

OH GOD... THE BARRIER WOULDN'T OPEN FOR ME... OBVIOUSLY THE BANK IS PLANNING TO FIRE ME AND HAS CANCELLED MY SECURITY ACCESS... I'M MAKING MYSELF SCARCE...

MEGABANK CAR PARK

REVERSE

SCREECH

Alex

PEATTIE + TAYLOR

Strip 1

Panel 1: CLIVE DIDN'T SHOW UP FOR WORK TODAY. NO ONE'S HEARD FROM HIM OR KNOWS WHERE HE IS...

Panel 2: WELL, CYRUS, MY GUESS IS THAT HE THINKS HE'S ON THE REDUNDANCY LIST, SO HE'S GONE INTO HIDING, KNOWING THAT YOU HAVE TO KEEP PAYING HIM UNTIL YOU GIVE HIM THE NEWS TO HIS FACE...

Panel 3: THAT'S A CRAZY THEORY, ALEX. WHAT MAKES YOU SAY THAT? NO REAL REASON, CYRUS...CALL IT A HUNCH... A GUT FEELING... A SHOT IN THE DARK...

Panel 4: SO YOU DIDN'T MENTION THAT CLIVE HAS UPDATED HIS PROFILE STATUS TO "UNEMPLOYED" ON FACEBOOK? AND ADMIT WE SPEND HALF OUR TIME SURFING THE INTERNET..? NO WAY...

Strip 2

Panel 1: SO CLIVE'S VANISHED? YES, IT SEEMS HIS SECURITY PASS WAS REFUSED ON MONDAY MORNING...

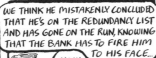

Panel 2: WE THINK HE MISTAKENLY CONCLUDED THAT HE'S ON THE REDUNDANCY LIST AND HAS GONE ON THE RUN, KNOWING THAT THE BANK HAS TO FIRE HIM TO HIS FACE... HOW CAN YOU BE SURE?

Panel 3: LOOK, HE'S GONE TO GROUND. NO ONE HAS HEARD FROM HIM. NOT EVEN HIS WIFE OR FAMILY... WHAT ABOUT HIS FRIENDS? HAS HE CONTACTED ANY OF THEM? THAT GOES WITHOUT SAYING...

Panel 4: YES... ALL OF US...WE'VE RECEIVED REQUESTS TO BE ADDED AS HIS CONNECTIONS ON "LINKED IN"... OH DEAR...PEOPLE ONLY RESORT TO THOSE PROFESSIONAL NETWORKING WEBSITES WHEN THEY'RE LOOKING FOR A JOB...

Strip 3

Panel 1: SO CLIVE THINKS HE'S ABOUT TO GET FIRED AND HAS GONE A.W.O.L.? THAT'S OUR UNDERSTANDING, SHELLEY...

HUMAN RESOURCES

Panel 2: HIS BLACKBERRY'S SWITCHED OFF, HE HASN'T BEEN HOME, NO ONE'S SEEN HIM OR HAS ANY IDEA WHERE HE IS... WHAT AN AWFUL SITUATION...

Panel 3: QUITE, AT TIMES LIKE THIS ONE HE DESPERATELY WISHES ONE COULD JUST GET A SHORT MESSAGE FROM HIM: TO LET US KNOW THAT HE'S OKAY AND HOW HE'S FEELING...

Panel 4: BUT NOT DOZENS OF THE BLASTED THINGS AT TEN MINUTE INTERVALS... YES, HE'S BEEN VERY ACTIVE ON "TWITTER" OF LATE... "CLIVE IS FEELING EMOTIONALLY FRAGILE" POSTED 3 MINUTES AGO...

Twitter

Strip 4

Panel 1: WELL, DOCTOR, ALL MY SYMPTOMS HAVE CLEARED UP AND IT'S THANKS TO YOU...

Panel 2: EVER SINCE I'VE SUSPECTED THAT MY BANK WAS PLANNING TO FIRE ME I'VE BEEN SUFFERING FROM ANXIETY, DEPRESSION AND NERVOUS EXHAUSTION, BUT NOW I'M FEELING 100% RECOVERED.

Panel 3: ER... HOLD ON... I'VE ONLY JUST GIVEN YOU YOUR PRESCRIPTION. YOU HAVEN'T ACTUALLY TAKEN ANY MEDICINE YET...

Panel 4: WHO NEEDS IT? NOW I'VE BEEN OFFICIALLY DIAGNOSED AS SUFFERING FROM STRESS, THE BANK WOULDN'T DARE FIRE ME IN CASE I SUED THEM... I'M GOING BACK...

Alex PEATTIE + TAYLOR

JUST A FEW WEEKS AGO WE BANKERS WERE CONSIDERED PUBLIC ENEMY NUMBER ONE, BUT NOW WE SEEM TO HAVE BEEN REHABILITATED...

WELL, I SUPPOSE PEOPLE'S ANGER HAS BEEN DIRECTED AGAINST POLITICIANS INSTEAD...

YES. AND WORKING IN THE CITY IS SUDDENLY SEEN AS A RESPECTABLE OCCUPATION AGAIN...

WHEN ONE THINKS HOW WE USED TO AVOID OWNING UP TO BEING BANKERS AT DRINKS PARTIES FOR FEAR OF THE UNWELCOME AND AGGRESSIVE ATTENTIONS IT WOULD ATTRACT...

YES.

FROM PEOPLE HASSLING US TO GET INTERNSHIPS FOR THEIR KIDS.

QUITE. ALL THAT'S NOW GOING TO START AGAIN SO WE'D BEST CONTINUE TO KEEP A LOW PROFILE.

Alex PEATTIE + TAYLOR

LIKE MANY BANKERS, JEREMY DIDN'T GET A BONUS THIS YEAR AND SO WE'VE HAD TO MAKE ALL SORTS OF CUTBACKS.

LISTEN TO MY WIFE...

IT'S AWFUL... I'VE HAD TO GET RID OF MY TENNIS COACH, CANCEL MY RIDING LESSONS AND I NOW ONLY GO TO THE HAIRDRESSER'S ONCE A WEEK...

SHE HAS NO IDEA OF THE GENUINE SUFFERING CAUSED BY THIS RECESSION...

SADLY, LIKE MANY CORPORATE WIVES SHE'S BEEN PERMITTED TO EXIST IN A STATE OF DELUSION, WITH NO UNDERSTANDING OF THE REALITIES OF LIFE...

SUCH AS THAT YOUR ACTUAL BONUSES WERE ALWAYS TWICE WHAT YOU EVER TOLD HER AND THE REST WENT INTO YOUR SECRET BANK ACCOUNT?

TO FUND MY SHOOTING, GOLF, LAP-DANCING ETC... AND THAT'S ALL GONE TOO... SIGH

Alex PEATTIE + TAYLOR

IN THE OLD DAYS, AT THE FIRST SIGN OF AN ECONOMIC DOWNTURN WE'D JUST FIRE HALF THE WORKFORCE AND HAVE DONE WITH IT...

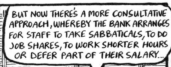

BUT NOW THERE'S A MORE CONSULTATIVE APPROACH, WHEREBY THE BANK ARRANGES FOR STAFF TO TAKE SABBATICALS, TO DO JOB SHARES, TO WORK SHORTER HOURS OR DEFER PART OF THEIR SALARY...

IT'S AN ARRANGEMENT THAT ALLOWS PEOPLE TO FEEL INCLUDED, VALUED AND EMPHASISES THAT THEY STILL HAVE A USEFUL ROLE TO PLAY HERE...

WHO?! THE H.R. DEPARTMENT?

EXACTLY... THEY KEEP THEMSELVES BUSY WITH ALL THIS NONSENSE SO WE DON'T GET ROUND TO FIRING THEM...

Alex PEATTIE + TAYLOR

NO ONE CAN WORK OUT IF THIS RECENT EQUITIES RALLY IS A BLIP OR THE START OF A NEW BULL RUN...

PRIVATELY MANY OF OUR PEOPLE ARE EXPRESSING RESERVATIONS, BUT THEY'RE AWARE THAT A ROBUST STOCK MARKET IS IMPORTANT FOR A GENERAL BUSINESS REVIVAL...

SO IT'S IMPORTANT FOR ALL OF US TO MAKE A PUBLIC SHOW THAT WE SEE A STRONG BULL MARKET AS A LONG-TERM TREND...

RIGHT...

WHICH IS WHY THE BANK IS ABOLISHING ITS FINAL SALARY PENSION SCHEME

WELL, OUR PEOPLE SHOULD BE CONFIDENT THAT THEIR MANAGED FUNDS WILL PAY OUT EVEN MORE IN THE END...

68

Strip 1

LOOK, MY NEW BLACKBERRY BOLD HAS ARRIVED. JUST IN TIME FOR MY HOLIDAYS NEXT WEEK..

OH YES..

IT'S GOT ALL THE FUNCTIONALITY OF THE TRADITIONAL BLACKBERRY, BUT WITH ADDED LIFESTYLE EXTRAS LIKE MUSIC, GAMES, VIDEOS ETC...

PERSONALLY I FIND THAT ALL A BIT GIMMICKY...

I PREFER THE OLD MACHINE WHICH WAS JUST A DULL, PRACTICAL BUSINESS TOOL WITH NO FLASHY EXTRAS.

YOU'RE JUST JEALOUS, ALEX...

NOT AT ALL...

WHAT? MY BLACKBERRY BATTERY'S GONE FLAT..

OH, THE KIDS WERE WATCHING MOVIES AND PLAYING GAMES ON IT IN THE CAR...

GRR... THIS COULD NEVER HAVE HAPPENED WITH THE OLD MODEL...

Strip 2

WELL, ALEX, I AM NOW A FULLY-QUALIFIED COUNSELLOR. IN THESE DIRE ECONOMIC TIMES PEOPLE ARE IN NEED OF SUPPORT...

HMM..

WITH RESPECT, PENNY, YOU'VE NEVER HAD TO WORK IN YOUR LIFE... YOU'VE ENJOYED THE COMFORTABLE, COSSETED LIFESTYLE OF A CORPORATE WIFE FOR THE LAST 20 YEARS...

SO?

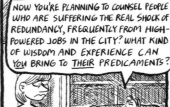

NOW YOU'RE PLANNING TO COUNSEL PEOPLE WHO ARE SUFFERING THE REAL SHOCK OF REDUNDANCY, FREQUENTLY FROM HIGH-POWERED JOBS IN THE CITY? WHAT KIND OF WISDOM AND EXPERIENCE CAN YOU BRING TO THEIR PREDICAMENTS?

WELL, YOU CAN MEET YOUR FRIENDS FOR COFFEE... I KNOW A LOVELY CAFÉ ON THE KING'S ROAD... AND YOU CAN TAKE TENNIS LESSONS... I CAN RECOMMEND A COACH...

THANKS, PENNY, AS AN EX-WORKAHOLIC I DIDN'T KNOW ANY OF THIS...

Strip 3

I SUPPOSE ONE OF THE REASONS WHY I TRAINED TO BE A COUNSELLOR WAS TO EARN ALEX'S RESPECT...

I MEAN, I WAS ALWAYS JUST THE STAY-AT-HOME WIFE OF THE IMPORTANT CORPORATE FINANCIER; AND WHEN HE CAME HOME IN THE EVENINGS HE'D ASK ME PATRONISINGLY ABOUT MY DAY..

BUT NOW THAT I'VE GOT A PROPER CAREER OF MY OWN IT PUTS ME ON AN EQUAL FOOTING WITH HIM. I FEEL IT'S REALLY IMPROVED OUR DOMESTIC RELATIONSHIP...

ISN'T IT GREAT, ALEX, THAT WE'VE NOW BOTH GOT JOBS THAT, FOR REASONS OF CLIENT CONFIDENTIALITY, WE'RE NOT ALLOWED TO TALK TO EACH OTHER ABOUT?

HMM...?

Strip 4

ENGLAND MANAGED TO FLUKE A TECHNICAL DRAW IN THE FIRST TEST MATCH DESPITE BEING COMPREHENSIVELY OUTPLAYED BY THE AUSSIES.

AND YET WE'RE TREATING IT AS A VICTORY AND BEING REALLY UPBEAT AND POSITIVE ABOUT THE REST OF THE SERIES... HAVE WE TOTALLY LOST OUR GRIP ON REALITY?

WELL, CRICKET IS SAID TO BE A METAPHOR FOR LIFE, CLIVE...

YES BUT HERE WE ARE: RATIONAL ADULTS, WILFULLY IGNORING ALL THE STATISTICAL EVIDENCE AND RELYING ON BLIND OPTIMISM...

EXACTLY..

JUST LIKE WITH ALL OUR BULLISH PRONOUNCEMENTS ON THE ECONOMY...

OH YES. WELL LET'S HOPE IT HOLDS UP BETTER THAN OUR CRICKET TEAM IS LIKELY TO...

Alex — PEATTIE + TAYLOR

Strip 1:

THE THING IS: I SUFFER FROM THESE VIOLENT MOOD SWINGS... I GO FROM ONE EXTREME TO THE OTHER...
I KNOW... YOU'VE TOLD ME...

THERE'S SOME DAYS WHEN I FEEL TOTALLY DEPRESSED AND PESSIMISTIC ABOUT EVERYTHING... THE COUNTRY IS BUST; THE ECONOMY IS HEADING FOR HYPERINFLATION... IT'S ALL BLEAK AND HOPELESS...

THEN IT'S SCARY, BUT A SHORT WHILE LATER I FEEL COMPLETELY THE _OPPOSITE_...

WHAT, TOTALLY PESSIMISTIC BECAUSE YOU THINK WE'RE FACING A DECADE OF _DEFLATION_?
YES... NONE OF US ECONOMISTS HAVE EVER BEEN MUCH GOOD AT PREDICTING THESE THINGS...
MAYBE THAT'S WHY YOU GOT SACKED...

Strip 2:

THE CREDIT CRUNCH HAS REALLY TAKEN ITS TOLL ON THE FINANCIAL SECTOR OVER THE LAST YEAR...

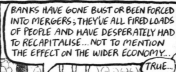
BANKS HAVE GONE BUST OR BEEN FORCED INTO MERGERS; THEY'VE ALL FIRED LOADS OF PEOPLE AND HAVE DESPERATELY HAD TO RECAPITALISE... NOT TO MENTION THE EFFECT ON THE WIDER ECONOMY...
TRUE...

BANKERS' INSTINCTIVE SHORT-TERMISM IS TO BLAME FOR ALL THIS, CLIVE, AND IT'S A MINDSET WE NEED TO REASSESS IN THE LIGHT OF THE SITUATION WE FIND OURSELVES IN...
YES...

WE'RE _PROFITABLE_ AGAIN: WE'VE GOT A LOWER COSTBASE, FEWER COMPETITORS AND LOTS OF FEES FROM DOING RIGHTS ISSUES TO RAISE EMERGENCY FUNDS FOR CLIENTS...
QUITE. SO, AS LONG AS ONE THINKS IN THE SHORT TERM, EVERYTHING'S ROSY...

Strip 3:

THERE'S PUBLIC ANGER AT BANKS ANNOUNCING BIG PROFITS SO SOON AFTER THEY WERE BAILED OUT BY THE TAXPAYER....

BUT ONE HAS TO REMEMBER THAT WHILE SOME BANKS PILED INTO THE RECKLESS DEBT CULTURE OF THE RECENT PAST, OTHERS STUCK WITH THEIR SENSIBLE OLD-FASHIONED BUSINESS MODEL...

SO IF BANKS LIKE OURS ARE NOW MAKING MONEY IT'S A REFLECTION OF HOW RESPONSIBLE OUR APPROACH WAS BACK IN THE YEARS OF EXCESS...
YES

BECAUSE WE ADVISED ALL OUR CLIENTS TO FUND RASH ACQUISITIONS BY BORROWING LOADS OF MONEY WHICH THEY NOW CAN'T AFFORD TO REPAY...
SO THEY'RE HAVING TO PAY US EVEN MORE IN FEES TO RESTRUCTURE THEIR DEBT...
THAT'S WHAT _I_ CALL PRUDENT PRACTICE.

Strip 4:

SO HOW ARE YOU FINDING YOUR NEW JOB AS A REDUNDANCY COUNSELLOR, PENNY?
TOUGHER THAN I'D IMAGINED...

I FIND I'M CONSTANTLY DEALING WITH MALE INSECURITY... WHERE A MAN WHO IS USED TO BEING THE PROVIDER FOR HIS FAMILY SUDDENLY HAS TO COPE WITH FEELINGS OF INADEQUACY AND IMPOTENCE...

HOW HE CAN STRUGGLE TO COME TO TERMS WITH HIS PERCEIVED LOSS OF AUTHORITY AND STATUS AND THE AWARENESS THAT HIS SOCIAL AND DOMESTIC ROLE HAS BEEN DEGRADED...

BUT, PENNY, HAVING A WIFE WHO WORKS... PEOPLE MIGHT THINK I'VE LOST MY JOB...
OH, GET OVER IT, ALEX...

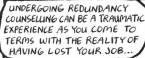

Strip 1

PLEASE... HELP YOURSELF TO A TISSUE... AND DON'T FEEL BAD ABOUT CRYING...

UNDERGOING REDUNDANCY COUNSELLING CAN BE A TRAUMATIC EXPERIENCE AS YOU COME TO TERMS WITH THE REALITY OF HAVING LOST YOUR JOB...

PARP

AND QUITE FREQUENTLY ALL SORTS OF PAINFUL MEMORIES AND ASSOCIATIONS CAN BE BROUGHT UP DURING THE COURSE OF A SESSION...

...BUT NOT NORMALLY BEFORE IT'S ACTUALLY STARTED...

I'M SORRY... IT'S JUST WHEN YOU ASKED ME IF I'D SWITCHED OFF MY BLACKBERRY AND I SUDDENLY REMEMBERED THAT I DON'T HAVE ONE ANY MORE...

SOB

Strip 2

WELL, THE FINANCIAL CRISIS IS ABATING AND THERE'S A GROWING OPTIMISM ABOUT THE FUTURE...

BUT THIS IS THE TIME TO PAUSE FOR REFLECTION AND ASK OURSELVES SHOULD WE JUST BLINDLY PURSUE THE SAME ECONOMIC POLICIES THAT CREATED THE CREDIT BUBBLE?

DO WE REALLY NEED TO INITIATE A NEW CONSUMER BOOM TO MOVE FORWARDS? IS BOOSTING G.D.P. THE ONLY WAY TO MEASURE SOCIETY'S PROGRESS? IS ECONOMIC GROWTH NECESSARILY BETTER THAN STABILITY?

HAS RUPERT BECOME A LIBERAL?!

NO, JUST MANAGING PEOPLE'S BONUS EXPECTATIONS...

Strip 3

THE AFTERMATH OF THE CREDIT CRUNCH HAS PRODUCED AN AWFUL SELF-RIGHTEOUSNESS IN THE CITY...

IN OUR DAY THE OBJECT WAS TO GET SOME ADVANTAGE OVER ONE'S COMPETITORS, BUT TODAY EVERYTHING IS SUPPOSED TO BE ABOUT FAIRNESS AND TRANSPARENCY...

WHEN PEOPLE TALK ABOUT CLIENT RELATIONS THEY JUST SPOUT INANE BUZZWORDS ABOUT STRIVING FOR "BALANCE", "FOCUS", "CLARITY" AND "LEVEL GROUND"...

MAKES SENSE TO ME...

RESTAURANT

WHOOPS! HOW'S YOUR BALANCE? ARE YOU ABLE TO FOCUS PROPERLY? CAN YOU SEE CLEARLY ENOUGH TO MAKE IT BACK TO YOUR OFFICE?

SWAY

WHOAH... THIS GROUND DOESN'T SEEM TO BE LEVEL, ALEX...

HIC

THANKS AGAIN FOR ALL THAT CONFIDENTIAL INFORMATION ABOUT YOUR COMPANY...

Strip 4

WHEN THE CREDIT CRUNCH HIT THE CITY LAST AUTUMN BANKS STOPPED SPENDING MONEY...

WELL IT LOOKED LIKE THE GLOBAL ECONOMY WAS BUST, PLUS WE HAD TO TAKE INTO ACCOUNT PUBLIC ANGER AT OUR PERCEIVED EXCESSES ...BUT THAT'S ALL CHANGING...

AS WE LOOK TO THE FUTURE WE'RE NOW SEEING BUSINESS TRAVEL PICKING UP AGAIN, CORPORATE SPONSORSHIP BEING RESUMED, CLIENT RELATIONSHIPS ONCE MORE ACTIVELY PURSUED...

SO YOU THINK THE ECONOMY'S RECOVERING?

OH, NO... IT'S COMPLETELY SCREWED... BUT OUR DEPARTMENTAL BUDGETS ARE REALLOCATED IN SEPTEMBER AND IF WE DON'T SPEND THIS YEAR'S WE'LL GET LESS NEXT TIME...

Strip 1

SO YOU'RE CELEBRATING GETTING A NEW JOB AT A BANK? NO DOUBT ON SOME EXTRAVAGANT REMUNER-ATION DEAL...

IT'S GENEROUS, YES...

IT JUST SHOWS THE FINANCIAL SECTOR HASN'T LEARNED ANYTHING FROM THE SUBPRIME CRISIS, WHERE THE LURE OF BIG BONUSES LED TO EXCESSIVE RISK-TAKING WHICH ENDED WITH SEVERAL BANKS GOING BUST...

DON'T WORRY. THERE'S NO CHANCE OF A REPEAT OF THAT. MY NEW BANK HAS STRUCTURED MY COMPENSATION PACKAGE SO THAT IN NO WAY AM I INCENTIVISED TO TAKE RISKS...

WELL: GOOD.

I'M ON A TWO-YEAR GUARANTEED BONUS... SO WHY WOULD I RISK BANKRUPTING MY EMPLOYER AND MISSING OUT ON THAT MONEY?

ESPECIALLY WHEN I CAN DO NOTHING AND GET IT ALL ANYWAY...

STUTTER

Strip 2

THE BEST THING ABOUT HAVING QUIT MY JOB IN THE CITY TO BECOME A TEACHER IS THE EIGHT-WEEK SUMMER HOLIDAY, ALEX...

LONG LAZY DAYS IN FRONT OF THE TV WITH THE CRICKET ON, JUST LIKE WHEN I WAS A BOY... OF COURSE, MY DAD WAS ALWAYS AT WORK SO WE NEVER GOT THE CHANCE TO WATCH IT TOGETHER...

WHICH IS WHY I DIDN'T WANT THAT PHYSICAL SEPARATION THING – WHERE ONE PERSON IS AWAY IN AN OFFICE – TO BE WHAT PREVENTED ME AND MY SON FROM BEING ABLE TO BOND TOGETHER OVER THE CRICKET...

SO COULD I HAVE A WORD WITH HIM PLEASE?

SORRY, NO... HE'S BUSY ON A SPREADSHEET...

TYPICAL... KIDS THESE DAYS ONLY CARE ABOUT BLASTED WORK EXPERIENCE...

Strip 3

I SUPPOSE IT WAS THE PROCESS OF BEING FIRED BY MY BOSS THAT WAS THE TOUGHEST BIT...

I HAD TO FIGHT BACK THE EMOTIONS THAT WERE WELLING UP IN ME AS HE BROKE THE NEWS. I WAS DETERMINED NOT TO ALLOW HIM TO SEE HOW IT WAS AFFECTING ME.

I DIDN'T WANT TO LET HIM HAVE THE SATISFACTION... BUT NOW I NEED TO GIVE VENT TO THE FEELINGS THAT COULDN'T FIND THEIR TRUE EXPRESSION...

WHAT WOULD HAVE BEEN THEIR TRUE EXPRESSION?

A HUGE EAR-TO-EAR GRIN BASICALLY... I ALREADY HAD ANOTHER JOB TO GO TO, YOU SEE... BUT I WAS WORRIED HE'D STOP MY REDUNDANCY CHEQUE.

ER... SO WHY EXACTLY ARE YOU HERE?

WELL MY BANK PAID FOR THIS COUNSELLING TOO... HEE HEE... THE MUGS...

Strip 4

SO THE GRADUATES WHO WERE DUE TO START WORK HERE IN THE AUTUMN HAVE BEEN SENT AWAY FOR A YEAR?

YES...

WELL, WITH THE ECONOMIC DOWNTURN WE'VE GOT NO JOBS FOR THEM AT PRESENT, SO WE'RE ADVISING THEM TO GO OFF AND GET SOME HANDS-ON EXPERIENCE, MAYBE SET UP A BUSINESS...

IT'S AN OPPORTUNITY FOR THEM TO HAVE A GO AT BEING ENTREPRENEURS. WHO KNOWS? SOME OF THEM MIGHT EVEN MAKE A SUCCESS OF IT...

AND WHAT ABOUT THE ONES WHO FAIL?

WELL, THEY CAN COME BACK AND BE BANKERS...

YES, AND ADVISE OTHER PEOPLE HOW TO RUN THEIR BUSINESSES...

Alex PEATTIE + TAYLOR

THIS AUTUMN'S INTAKE OF GRADUATES HAVE BEEN TOLD THAT THEIR JOBS ARE BEING DEFERRED FOR A YEAR...

YES...

IT'S HARDLY A POSITIVE SIGN, CLIVE. IT SHOWS THE BANK IS CUTTING BACK STAFF AND, MORE IMPORTANTLY, THAT IT IS FAILING TO INVEST IN ITS FUTURE...

THE SELF-BELIEF OF PEOPLE IN OUR ORGANISATION IS FRAGILE AT THE BEST OF TIMES AND THIS NEWS IS BOUND TO HAVE AN EFFECT ON GENERAL MORALE...

WHEW... THAT'S GIVEN US A BIT OF A CUSHION...

NICE TO KNOW THERE WON'T BE ANYONE COMING UP THROUGH THE SYSTEM TO TAKE OUR JOBS FOR A WHILE...

GRADUATE PROGRAM

alex@alexcartoon.com

Alex PEATTIE + TAYLOR

YOU BANKERS ARE ALL VERY BULLISH ON THE ECONOMY. THAT'S BECAUSE YOU PERSONALLY BENEFIT FROM IT...

IN WHAT WAY?

I MEAN A RISING MARKET IS GOOD FOR BUSINESS WHICH MEANS YOU GET BIG BONUSES...

BUT OUR BANK HAS STATED THAT THERE WILL BE NO BONUSES THIS YEAR...

YOU SEE, BONUSES EVOLVED AS A WAY TO KEEP BANKS FLEXIBLE BY MAINTAINING A LOW COST-BASE. IN GOOD YEARS EMPLOYEES GET WELL PAID, IN BAD YEARS THEY GET NOTHING...

PEOPLE HAVE TENDED TO FORGET THIS FACT...

YES..

PARTICULARLY THE BANKS, WHEN THEY MADE UP FOR THIS YEAR'S BONUS SHORTFALL BY DOUBLING EVERYONE'S SALARIES...

WHICH MEANS IF THERE'S ANOTHER DOWNTURN THE ONLY WAY TO CUT COSTS WILL BE TO FIRE US ALL...

THAT'S WHY WE NEED TO TALK THE MARKET UP...

alex@alexcartoon.com

Alex PEATTIE + TAYLOR

SOME OF OUR ANALYSTS ARE COMPLAINING BECAUSE THE BANK WON'T PUBLISH THEIR RESEARCH...

THAT'S BECAUSE THEY'RE TOO NEGATIVE ON THE ECONOMY. THINGS ARE TOUGH FOR THE BANK RIGHT NOW AND WE NEED OUR PEOPLE TO TALK THE MARKET UP AND GET CLIENTS DEALING...

WE COULD REMIND EMPLOYEES THAT THERE'S ALWAYS THE BANK'S VOLUNTARY REDUNDANCY SCHEME. WE'D CONSIDER APPLICATIONS FROM ANY OF OUR ANALYSTS..

OF COURSE...

BUT SAY NO, OBVIOUSLY...

WELL, YES.. ANY OF THEM WHO IS CONFIDENT OF GETTING A NEW JOB MUST BE OPTIMISTIC ABOUT THE ECONOMY... -IE: JUST THE SORT OF DELUDED FOOL WE NEED TO KEEP HOLD OF...

alex@alexcartoon.com

Alex PEATTIE + TAYLOR

HOORAY... IT'S MY LAST DAY OF WORK EXPERIENCE TODAY... NO MORE BEING BOSSED AROUND BY YOU, ALEX...

I'M OFF ON MY HOLS TOO, TOM... WE'RE GOING DOWN TO OUR PLACE IN CORNWALL..

WHAT, A SEVEN-HOUR SWEATY DRIVE STUCK IN FRIDAY AFTERNOON TRAFFIC JAMS ALL DAY? RATHER YOU THAN ME...

ACTUALLY WE'RE FLYING DOWN LATER THIS EVENING...

BUT ISN'T IT USEFUL TO HAVE A CAR WHEN YOU'RE THERE SO YOU CAN GET AROUND?

OH... MOST DEFINITELY...

YOUR CAR'S OUTSIDE, ALEX... AH, THANKS FOR DRIVING IT DOWN FOR ME, TOM...

Arrivals

WELCOME TO CORNWALL

GOOD LUCK HITCH-HIKING BACK TO LONDON.

alex @ alexcartoon.com

ALEX HOLIDAYED IN BRITAIN.

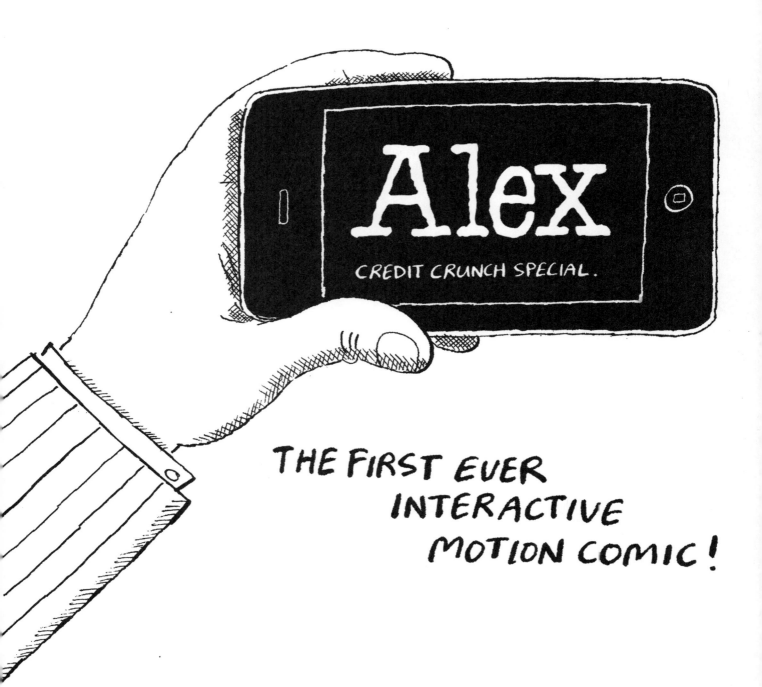

Also available from Masterley Publishing

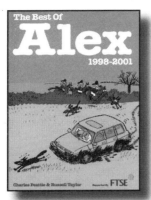

The Best of Alex 1998 - 2001
Boom to bust via the dotcom bubble.

The Best of Alex 2002
Scandals rock the corporate world.

The Best of Alex 2003
Alex gets made redundant.

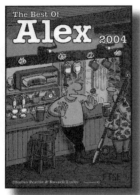

The Best of Alex 2004
And gets his job back.

The Best of Alex 2005
Alex has problems with the French.

The Best of Alex 2006
Alex gets a new American boss.

The Best of Alex 2007
Alex restructures Christmas.

The Best of Alex 2008
The credit crunch bites.

Celeb
Wrinkly rockstar Gary Bloke.

Mrs Moneypenny Returns
Columns from the FT.

All books cost £9.99 plus p+p.

Cartoon Orignals and Prints: All our cartoon originals are for sale.
They measure 4 x 14 inches. Prints are also available. All originals and
prints are signed by the creators.

For further details on prices and delivery charges for books, cartoons or
merchandise: **Alex, PO Box 39447, London N10 3WA**
Tel: 020 8374 1225 Fax: 0871 750 2343
Email: alex@alexcartoon.com Web: www.alexcartoon.com